'What is your name, child?' Jake asked, quite gently.

'Clem——' the boy began, and stopped, biting his lip. He spoke again an instant later, his tone more definite. 'Clem.'

One of his lordship's eyebrows went up. 'Clem. I see. How neat.' He paused a moment, but the boy said nothing. 'You will have to learn that you do not have to deal with a fool.'

Lashes fluttered over the wide eyes. 'I don't know what you mean. Please... won't you let me go?'

Lord Sothern took that small chin between his fingers once more, and his thumb caressed it. 'Very prettily phrased, my child. But I regret I cannot possibly let you go... Clementina.'

Elizabeth Bailey grew up in Malawi, Africa, returning to England only to plunge into the theatre. After many happy years 'tatting around the reps' and doing every kind of odd job under the sun in between, she finally turned from 'dabbling' to serious writing.

She finds it more satisfying than mere acting for she is in control of everything; scripts, design, direction, and the portrayal of every character! But Elizabeth still teaches drama to GCSE students. She lives in London, and SWEET SACRIFICE is her first novel for the Masquerade series.

SWEET
SACRIFICE

Elizabeth Bailey

*First published in Great Britain 1991
by Mills & Boon Limited*

© Elizabeth Bailey 1991

*Australian copyright 1991
Philippine copyright 1991
This edition 1991*

ISBN 0 263 77389 2

*Masquerade is a trademark published by
Mills & Boon Limited, Eton House,
18–24 Paradise Road, Richmond, Surrey, TW9 1SR.*

*Set in Times Roman 11 on 11½ pt.
04-9109-62080 C*

Made and printed in Great Britain

CHAPTER ONE

THE figure came upon them suddenly. Out of the night it hurtled, darting from a dark alleyway, a stout stick raised before it. There was a scuffle, a sharp cry of pain, and then the figure was squirming in my lord's iron hold, with the weapon lying harmless in the road.

'By God, it's a scandal!' ejaculated one of these late-night revellers. He planted his large feet squarely apart to steady his rocking frame, and shoved indignant thumbs into the pockets of the mustard-coloured waistcoat that met unsatisfactorily over a protruding belly. 'You daren't put your nose outside your door these days but some scoundrel is like to set upon you with a cudgel.' His somewhat bleary gaze eyed the prisoner with disfavour. 'Only a young 'un at that, if my eyes don't deceive me.'

'Like as they are to do so at this hour, I believe in this instance you are not mistaken, Harry,' drawled his lordship. 'Keep still, whelp!' This to the still struggling captive. He seized the boy's chin in one hand and forced his face up to the light of the nearby streetlamp.

Wide, scared eyes looked back at him out of pinched, white features. He could feel the trembling of the limbs under his steel grip. He did not think this was due to the chill of the April night.

'A sight too young for this game, are you not, my lad?'

'I w-wasn't—I didn't——' the boy faltered.

'What the devil were you about attacking three grown men single-handed?'

'I didn't. I'm not a thief.'

My lord's eyes narrowed, his gaze intent on the boy's young face. But before he could speak his friend intervened.

'Give him up to the watch, Sothern,' said Sir Harry. 'Newgate's the place for these rascals.'

The third man had been hovering on the outskirts, gathering his scattered wits. A slighter man than Blaine, and rather less the worse for drink, he was nevertheless in no condition easily to sustain shocks of this nature. His overcoat was unbuttoned, his slouch felt hat askew, but his speech was unslurred as he addressed his friend.

'Oh, come, Blaine. A bit extreme, surely.' He peered closely at the captive. 'It's little more than a child, and he didn't get anything off us, after all.'

'I didn't want anything off you,' uttered the boy, indignant now. 'I'm not a thief, I tell you. Let me go!' He pulled desperately, but unavailingly, away from the tight grip on his arm.

'And I suppose that stick of yours was not meant to hit one of us over the head, eh?' demanded Sir Harry in wrathful tones, his florid cheeks, witness to the liquor he had recently imbibed, reddening still further. 'By God, if I ever heard anything to equal the impertinence! Fetch him to the law officers, Jake, and be done with him.'

Lord Sothern glanced down from his superior height and shook his head. 'No. I've a surer way of dealing with him than our incompetent officers of the law.'

Sir Harry gave a crack of rude laughter. 'I'll warrant you have. You picked the wrong man for your tricks, boy.'

'What do you mean to do, Jake?' asked the other man curiously.

'Oh, nothing of great moment, Theo. Poetic justice, merely. I'll thrash the brat with his own weapon, and send him on his way.'

The boy gave a gasp of fright. Panic lent him strength, and he wrenched himself from Lord Sothern's slightly slackened hold. But instead of taking to his heels he ran into the road, seized his stick and turned to face them like a dog at bay.

'Come one step forward and I'll—I'll——'

Sir Harry Blaine and the Honourable Theodore Farleigh stared in astonishment, but Lord Sothern raised one eyebrow, faintly ironic.

'Very heroic, my young friend. But a trifle foolish, don't you think?'

The boy brandished his stick. 'I don't care! I won't be punished for a thief. I meant no harm, I tell you. I was—I was running from—from someone. And—and I didn't see you. Any of you. Until I cannoned into you like that.'

'A likely tale!' scoffed Sir Harry.

'It's true! And if you come near me I *will* hit you on the head.'

'It's plausible, Harry,' Theo suggested, interrupting his friend's vociferous expostulation at the boy's words. 'What do you make of it, Jake?'

Lord Sothern did not answer. He was watching the boy, dark eyes steady on the childish features as he took in the treble voice with its genteel quality of speech that had apparently escaped the notice of his friends. He stepped slowly forward, holding out a hand.

'Come, child. You are being quite absurd, you know. You cannot possibly overcome even one of us, let alone three.'

'Maybe not,' the boy conceded, 'but if I go down I'll go down fighting.'

With which, he aimed a blow that connected with Lord Sothern's leg. His lordship's furious oath rang in the silent street. Next moment the stick had gone flying and he had the boy overpowered once more.

'Now, brat,' he snapped, 'are you going to behave, or do I have to beat you into submission?'

The boy's eyes flashed defiance.

'You may have got the better of me now. But if you don't let me go you will be sorry presently.'

His lordship's swift anger died, and he laughed. 'That remains to be seen. But if you won't quieten down you will most assuredly get the thrashing you deserve.'

A strangled sob escaped the boy, and the fight went out of him. Swallowing on rising tears, he lifted his chin and stared back at his captor.

'Very well. Do with me as you will. But I am *not* a thief.'

'We'll see that in due course. But I cannot discuss the matter in the street at two o'clock in the morning. Besides, it is growing cold. We will repair to my house.'

'No!' Real alarm sounded in the boy's voice. 'No, I won't go with you!'

'You will come with me if I have to drag you all the way. Or carry you there, if need be.'

'Hold a moment, Jake,' Theo Farleigh interrupted. 'What are you about, man? We took no harm of the boy. Let him go.'

'No, by God!' Sir Harry said. 'To the law officers with him, say I.'

But nothing either could say moved Lord Sothern from his purpose. Amid the unceasing protests of both friends, and the boy's intermittent pleas to be released, he traversed the few streets that lay between them and his town residence in Albemarle Street. At his door he turned to bid his friends goodnight.

'By God, I believe you've taken leave of your senses,' blustered Sir Harry. 'What do you want with the varmint?'

'Harry is in the right of it, Jake. Let the boy go,' Theo said for what must have been the fiftieth time. 'You can want nothing from him.'

'On the contrary,' Jake said cheerfully. 'He has aroused my curiosity.' He grinned at the uncomprehending looks on his friends' faces. 'You are really very unobservant, both of you.'

The boy glanced sharply at him, the fear returning to his face. Keeping his hold on the boy's wrist, Sothern drew him closer.

'A young boy, a *very* young boy—a boy of obvious gentility if you will but observe him closely—flies into our midst in the early hours of the morning, and protests his innocence of intended robbery.' He smiled as Sir Harry and Theo gazed at the captive with new interest. 'There is a tale to be learned here, I think. And I, my dear friends, intend to learn it.'

The boy drew back, turning his face from the blatant curiosity of the other two gentlemen.

'Jupiter, I believe you are right, Jake!' exclaimed Theo Farleigh. 'Let us all go in and find out at once.'

'Oh, no. This is my game. And I'll play it alone.'

'Well, by God, that's too much!' exploded Sir Harry. 'Now see here, Sothern. The boy attacked us just as much as you——'

'But he did not attack us, Harry,' Jake said gently. 'We have his word on this. Besides, it was I he ran into, and it is I who will wrest his secret from him.'

Laughing, he pulled the boy after him into the house and shut the door on his friends' protests. An oil-lamp burned on a table. Still holding on to his prisoner's wrist, Lord Sothern opened a door into a small parlour, then took up the lamp and drew the boy into the room. He crossed to the mantelshelf and put the lamp down so that it threw brightness over them both.

'And now, my young friend, let me look at you,' he said, turning.

He let go of the boy's wrist at last. Throwing off the cloak and hat he wore, he cast them carelessly on to a chair. Then he took the boy by the shoulders and held him in the light. A cluster of ragged reddish curls fell about a piquant face with the look of an urchin. Wide eyes, their colour indeterminate in this uncertain light, stared gravely back at him.

'What is your name, child?' he asked, quite gently.

'Clem——' the boy began, and stopped, biting his lip. He spoke again an instant later, his tone more definite. 'Clem.'

One of his lordship's eyebrows went up. 'Clem. I see. How neat.' He paused a moment, but the boy said nothing. 'You will have to learn that you do not have to deal with a fool.'

Lashes fluttered over the wide eyes. 'I don't know what you mean. Please . . . won't you let me go?'

Lord Sothern took that small chin between his fingers once more and his thumb caressed it. 'Very prettily phrased, my child. But I regret I cannot possibly let you go . . . Clementina.'

Clementina gasped and drew back. Her tone was hushed.

'How did you know?'

Lord Sothern smiled. 'It wasn't difficult. You make far too pretty a boy, and——' A gesture indicated the budding woman's figure beneath the buff-breeches and the tightly fastened frock-coat.

'But your friends—the other gentlemen——'

'Are far too drunk to notice. Tonight, in any event. Tomorrow, however, is another matter.'

Clementina backed a step or two, the wide eyes dilating.

'Tomorrow? They won't see me tomorrow. Or ever!'

'Oh, I think they will. I always permit my friends to meet my mistress, you know.'

Blankly, Clementina gazed at him. Then she turned and raced for the door. In three strides Jake had caught up with her, and she was once again struggling madly in his hold.

'You don't escape me that easily, my dear,' he said softly, and crushed her to him, arms pinioned so that she could not move.

Ever resourceful, Clementina kicked him on the shin. He cursed, but did not loosen his hold. Instead his head came down and his mouth was on hers in a kiss so hard and so sudden that shock held her momentarily still.

Equally suddenly Lord Sothern released her, but he leaned his big shoulders against the door to prevent her getting out.

Breathing hard, Clementina backed off, her eyes darting about the room in search of a suitable weapon.

'You wait!' she panted. 'I will make you sorry you ever dared to touch me. You're a brute and a devil and I hate you!'

Jake laughed. 'Faith, I believe you had no need of this lesson, after all.'

Her eyes alighting on a heavy candlestick set upon a side-table, Clementina dashed across and lifted it, turning to face her tormentor.

Lord Sothern threw up his hands. 'I surrender!'

He walked forward and calmly wrested the candlestick from her grasp, returning it to its place.

'Come, Clementina, peace! Cry friends. See? I
will not touch you if only you don't try to run away
from me again.'

He held his hands away, and waited while she
eyed him uncertainly.

'If you try to make love to me . . .' Clementina
shook a fist.

Jake shook his head. 'I thought—mistakenly it
seems—that you needed a lesson on the dangers of
your masquerade. But I see that you are quite
capable of looking after yourself.'

'Yes, I am,' Clementina averred crossly. 'Why
do you imagine I was running so hard when I ran
into you?'

Jake raised an eyebrow. 'Am I to infer some other
man had penetrated your disguise?'

'At the inn, yes. Where I was to have stayed the
night, you understand. He—he pretended to be
friendly, and gave me wine to drink so that I might
not resist him. But I poured it down my arm. And
the second glass I threw in his face,' Clementina
related on a note of satisfaction. 'Then I hit him
on the head with the bottle, and ran away.'

Lord Sothern's shoulders shook. 'You are certainly a formidable adversary. But it won't do,
Clementina.' The smile left his face, and the dark
eyes became serious. 'You are an extraordinarily
brave girl, my dear, but you are still vulnerable.
You must realise that if I chose at this moment to
do my worst you would have little chance against
me.'

Clementina bit her lip, defiance warring with her innate honesty. 'I—I would not give in without a struggle.'

'Undoubtedly not,' he said gently, 'but withstand me you could not.'

A sigh escaped her. 'Oh, how I wish I were a man!'

Jake hid a smile and moved forward. 'Come, Clementina, sit down and let us discuss what is to be done with you.'

'If you will only let me go I will do very well by myself,' Clementina said with returning spirit. But she came to the light and perched warily on the edge of the comfortable armchair he indicated.

Lord Sothern took up a stance before the empty fireplace, and stood looking down at her.

'Now, let me have it all. Your full name and the name of the school you have undoubtedly run away from.'

'School?' exclaimed Clementina indignantly, her chin going up. 'I am not a schoolgirl, sir. I am nineteen.'

One of Jake's eyebrows went up. 'Indeed?'

The chin was lowered. 'Well, almost nineteen.'

Lord Sothern said nothing, but his expression was enough.

'Oh, very well, I am turned eighteen,' confessed Clementina crossly. 'But I am not a schoolgirl, and I wish you would not keep staring at me in that superior fashion as if you did not believe a word I said.'

'Should I?' But Jake's amusement could not be entirely suppressed. His smile had the effect of ruffling still further Clementina's already offended sensibilities.

'I will have you know, sir, I do not tell lies. And if you are going to disbelieve everything I say I shall say nothing further.'

Lord Sothern schooled his features to solemnity. 'My apologies, child. Very well, you are eighteen. I beg your pardon, almost nineteen, and you have not run away from school. Pray continue.'

'I am not going to tell you anything else,' Clementina said.

'Even if I promise to believe everything you say?'

'I don't care. I have just realised what you are at, and I know exactly what will happen if I tell you. You will try to take me back, and I am never going back.'

Lord Sothern pulled forward a straight-backed wooden chair and sat down, taking her hands and holding them in a firm clasp. 'Clementina, whatever the reason for your flight, there must be a solution. Only consider how concerned your parents must be for your safety.'

'Well, they are not, because I have not got any,' Clementina announced triumphantly.

'Your guardians, then,' pursued Jake.

Clementina's lips tightened, and she pulled her hands away. 'He—*they*—deserve no consideration from me. They have shown *me* none.'

Lord Sothern had not missed the slip, but he gave no sign, hoping that more would be revealed if he approached the matter indirectly.

'Very well. Having run away, where were you headed? Are you going to meet someone, perhaps? Or——'

'I am not eloping, if that is what you think.'

'In those clothes? Hardly.'

'Well, but I could not run away dressed as a girl, could I?'

'You should not have run away at all.'

'Much you know about it. You would not say so if you knew the truth.'

'Try me.'

Clementina opened her mouth and shut it again, glowering at him. 'I am not to be caught by such a trick as that, sir. And I do not know why you ask me all these questions. It is no concern of yours, after all. And you have not even the common courtesy to introduce yourself, even though you have abducted me.'

Jake rose. 'I beg your pardon, ma'am. James, Lord Sothern, wholly at your service.'

Clementina stared. 'Are you the Earl of Sothern?'

Jake bowed.

'Dear Lord! You don't behave at all as one would expect.'

Lord Sothern covered his eyes briefly with one hand. 'Ah, my reputation! Alas, alas! I had no idea my notoriety had spread so far as—where was it you came from?'

Clementina's eyes flashed. 'You must take me for a fool, my lord!'

'That I don't. You are the wiliest young lady I have ever encountered.'

Clementina was silent for a moment, considering him, her head tilted to one side.

'If you will not let me go what do you propose to do with me?'

'A good question,' Jake said on a rueful note.

'Well, you cannot keep me here, can you? People would be bound to talk, and you cannot want any more of that.'

'No, my God!'

'There you are, then. You will have to let me go.'

'Or I could marry you,' Sothern said thoughtfully.

'What?' gasped Clementina. 'Oh, no! I am not at all the right person for a countess. Besides,' she added candidly, 'you are far too old.'

'Thank you,' said Jake faintly.

'After all, I am only eighteen, and——'

'Almost nineteen,' corrected his lordship.

'And you,' continued Clementina, unheeding, 'must be very nearly thirty years of age.'

'One foot in the grave, in fact.' Jake sighed. 'I had not considered it before, but you are perfectly right. How depressing!'

'Well, then?'

Sothern smiled at her. 'Well, then, I think the best course would be for me to become your guardian—temporarily, of course.'

Clementina looked at him, expressionless. 'People would say you had run mad. And who would believe it when they see me living in your house without even the vestige of a chaperon?'

'Ah, but they won't see you living in my house. As for a chaperon, why I think that may be arranged.' He held out a hand to her. 'Come along, my young friend.'

Clementina rose, but eyed him suspiciously. 'Where are you taking me?'

'To find a bed. Oh, not here,' he added, laughing at her expression. 'I have a most respectable arrangement in mind.'

'Grandmama!'

The Dowager Lady Staplegrove awoke with a jerk, and lay blinking at the shadowed face leaning over her.

'Grandmama, wake up!'

The mists of sleep receded a little. She raised herself on one elbow, and peered at the intruder.

'Sothern? Is that you?'

'Yes, it's I. Do wake up.'

Jake took her urgently by the shoulders, and drew her to sit up.

'What is amiss? What is amiss?' she asked anxiously, her fingers automatically reaching up to straighten her lace nightcap.

'Nothing is amiss, but——'

There was a sharp hissing of breath. 'Nothing? Then what the deuce do you mean by waking me up in the middle of the night, sir? Have you taken leave of your senses?'

'Probably,' Jake responded, a laugh in his voice.

Lady Staplegrove reached out for the candle by her bed which her grandson had relit. She lifted it, and examined his face closely. Then she sniffed at him.

'Brandy. I thought as much. You are intoxicated, sir. How dare you bring your sordid revelry into my home?'

Lord Sothern took the candle from her, and replaced it on the bedside-table next to the volume she had been reading before she went to sleep. Not, as might have been supposed of an elderly lady, a book of sermons or the Bible, he noted with a fleeting inward amusement, but one of Miss Smith's romantic tales entitled *Emmeline*. He leaned over and kissed her on the cheek.

'Dear Grandmama, I am not intoxicated. I love you far too much to trouble you with my drunken ravings.'

'I want none of your cajolery, rascal.' But her ladyship was softening. 'If you are not drunk, what in the world are you doing here at this unseasonable hour?'

'I want your help, Grandmama.'

'My help?' Lady Staplegrove took his wrist in a surprisingly strong grip. 'Sothern, you have not killed your man?'

'Nothing like that, ma'am,' Jake said soothingly. 'If you will allow me——'

'Then you have created some scandal, I'll be bound.' With a resigned sigh Lady Staplegrove leaned back among her cushions. 'Well, man? Out with it. It is a woman, I suppose?'

'As a matter of fact, yes, but it is not in the least——'

'I knew it! Lord above, Sothern! When will you abandon these wild ways of yours and settle down?

As a rule, I say nothing about these exploits of yours——'

'Oh, don't you just!' retorted Jake. 'But before you ring your peal over me, Grandmama, allow me to say that you are mistaken. This time I am to be commended. My actions were dictated by the purest chivalry.'

'I wish I may live to see it! But by all means tell me all about it.'

'I will do so if you will give me a chance.'

'Very well, very well. But be quick. I am an old woman, and much in need of my beauty-sleep. Not that there is much to be gained by that at my age.'

'Grandmama!' Jake exploded. 'Will you listen to me?'

Lady Staplegrove flung out a hand. 'Get on, then.'

She was at first inclined to be indignant when she learned that Lord Sothern expected her to house an unknown waif who was so lost to all sense of propriety as to wear breeches in the streets. But as Jake related the brief tale she warmed to the girl. Anyone, especially a female, who could show so much spirit excited her admiration.

'She kicked you, you say?'

'Very efficiently,' Jake corroborated ruefully.

'Ah!' she said, on a note of satisfaction. 'In that case I shall be delighted to house her.'

'Thank you,' Jake said, not without a touch of irony.

'Where is she?' demanded her ladyship.

'In the pink parlour downstairs.'

'And what makes you think she has not run away again? Or indeed, that she will not do so as soon as your back is turned?'

Jake considered this. 'Well, I don't know. I suspect that now she knows she has nothing to fear from me she is bent on making use of my protection. After all, she is aware of the dangers of her situation. I don't know what her plans may have been, but it is apparent that she has now abandoned them. For the moment, at least.'

'Hm. And she will tell you nothing of her circumstances?'

'Not yet. Between us, perhaps, you and I may discover something. If not, I suppose I must set about an investigation.'

Lady Staplegrove raised her brows in a gesture very reminiscent of her grandson's own habit. 'And how will you do that?'

'Oh, I shan't. I shall set Cullen on to check all the likely seminaries for a runaway.'

'You hold by your belief that she has run away from school, then?'

'It seems likely. You may judge differently, of course, when you meet her.'

'Meet her? Gracious heaven, what are we about?' exclaimed her ladyship, pulling back her covers and getting out of bed. 'All this time that poor child has been waiting for you downstairs. Go at once and tell her I shall be down directly. No, stay. Hand me my robe, and I will accompany you.'

In the pink parlour downstairs Clementina was growing momently more anxious. Lord Sothern had not told her whose house this was, and she began

to fear that he had betrayed her. Could he have
decided to hand her over to one of his friends,
perhaps? Or even—and her toes curled at the
thought—to sell her services to some brothel-
keeper? Common sense told her that this was unlikely. Brook Street was hardly the right locality for
a house of ill repute. And the quality of the pink
brocaded chairs with the matching curtains of the
room, even in the ill light afforded by the single
branch of candles lit by the elderly butler who had
let them in, spoke clearly of gentility.

Even so, Clementina wondered if she had made
a mistake to trust Jake. His assessment of her state
of mind was not far wrong. Hers had been an im-
pulsive flight, little thought out. Originally she had
intended only to pass through London in order to
board the stagecoach for Norwich. Once in
London, however, and with time to think, she had
realised that the first place they would think of
looking for her would be Dunhythe. Discouraged,
and beginning to be a little frightened, she had then
found herself the target of the unwelcome advances
of the man at the inn where she was waiting to catch
the stagecoach early next morning.

Lord Sothern's sudden entry into her schemes
had seemed at first disastrous. She dreaded to think
of the outcome had they given her up to the law
officers as Sir Harry Blaine had suggested. Instead,
Sothern had dragged her to his home because, it
now transpired, he had guessed her secret and
meant to rescue her from her own folly.

Well, it might be to her advantage, perhaps, to
accept his assistance. At least it would give her time

to think, to work out a plan of campaign. Better yet, she could stay here a few days to give her pursuers time to search for her at Dunhythe. Not finding her, they would give up. Then she might go there to seek refuge with Margery.

Another thought struck her. In London it might be possible to get in touch with her family's man of business. He might be able to help her. She was sure he could know nothing of the plans that had been made for her future. Not that she would have minded them, if only...

Her hurrying thoughts were interrupted by the opening of the door behind her. Clementina turned to see an elderly lady come in, clad in a nightcap and a dressing-gown of startling hue with a design of peacocks, and carrying a lighted candle. Behind her stood the Earl.

'Ah, so you have not run away again,' he said smiling.

'Of course she has not,' scoffed Lady Staplegrove, handing him her candle. 'Where would she go?' She came forward, and took the girl's hands in a warm clasp. 'My poor, dear child! Gracious, how cold you are! You must come up-stairs at once. Murray shall put a warming-pan in your bed. You will have the bedchamber next to mine, my dear, and so be comfortable. Ring the bell, Sothern.'

But Jake had already done so, and the butler entered almost before her ladyship had finished speaking. Although he had opened the front door somewhat scantily clad in hastily thrown on jacket and breeches, he had by now found time to don correct attire, complete with lace cravat and powdered wig.

'Ah, Dorridge,' the Dowager hailed him. 'Fetch Murray to me at once. And have a fire made up in the bedchamber next my own. Oh, yes, and some milk. Hot, if you please. At once, Dorridge.'

'Certainly, my lady,' uttered the butler, apparently unsurprised by the sudden appearance in the early hours of her ladyship's grandson with an unexpected guest, or by the orders so haphazardly thrown at him.

'Admirable creature,' said Lady Staplegrove as he left the room. 'Now, my dear child, come with me.'

'One moment, ma'am,' interrupted Sothern, as she took her candle from him. 'We have both been remiss. Clementina, allow me to present Lady Staplegrove, my grandmother.'

'Yes, yes, how stupid of me! I am the Dowager Lady Staplegrove, child.'

'H-how do you do, ma'am?' Clementina faltered, rather taken aback.

'Better than you, I fancy. Now Sothern has told me all about you, so there is no need for us to discuss anything at all tonight. We will have you tucked up as soon as may be, and fast asleep in bed—where we all ought to be, I may say.'

'Thank you, ma'am. You are very kind.'

'Oh, tush, child! I am nothing of the sort. We shall take cold if we remain in this chill. Come along.' Her ladyship swept to the door, and stopped short as she came up against her grandson. 'What in the world are you waiting for, Sothern? Go away, do. You may call and see Clementina tomorrow. We shall certainly have to see about some clothes.'

Quite overwhelmed, Clementina began to follow her. She turned at the door to smile a little shyly at Jake.

'I—I didn't think—that is, I had no idea——' She swallowed and tried again. 'I thought you might have tricked me. You never said this was your grandmother's house.'

Jake walked forward, smiling. 'I only make my own scandals, Clementina. I don't create them for innocent young ladies.' He took her fingers in his, and lightly kissed them. 'Sleep well.'

Lady Staplegrove reappeared and took hold of Clementina's arm. 'Come on, child, do. I can't abide dawdlers.' She led Clementina away.

Lord Sothern let himself out of the house, and walked thoughtfully back to his own home. About to put his key into the lock, he was surprised to find the door opened to him by his own porter.

'What in Hades are you doing up at this hour, Cheswick?'

'I was woken, my lord, by this individual here, who insists on having speech with you.'

Cheswick's disapproval was patent. Lord Sothern turned. A man in a frieze greatcoat was perched rather uncomfortably on the edge of one of the straight-backed hall chairs. He rose as he encountered his lordship's eye.

'Who are you? What do you want with me?' Jake demanded in a peremptory tone.

The man touched his forelock. 'Toby Creech, me lord. Bow Street.'

'Bow Street?'

'That's right, me lord. Begging yer lordship's pardon for the intrusion like, but I understand as how yer lordship has apprehended a young gentleman.'

'Oh, you do, eh? Well?'

The man coughed. 'Seemingly, me lord, by the description this would be a young fellow we're after. A Master Clem Henlow.'

CHAPTER TWO

SIR HARRY BLAINE was breakfasting when Sothern burst in on him in his lodgings later that morning.

'Harry, I've a good mind to call you out,' Jake told him, taking a chair and coolly helping himself to a cup of coffee.

Sir Harry blinked at him. 'What the devil for, old fellow? Wasn't flirting with Matilda again, was I?' He frowned in an effort of memory. 'No, can't have been. Card party. She wasn't there.'

Lord Sothern eyed him dispassionately. 'Yes, I suppose it was too much to hope that you would remember. I had better have gone to Theo.'

'You may as well tell me all about it now you're here,' invited his friend, plunging his fork into another slice of beef, and stuffing it into his mouth.

'You're a hog, Harry,' Jake remarked. 'You'll be as fat as a flawn before you're thirty—with one foot in the grave.' A reminiscent smile curved his lips. 'And far too old to marry a young lady of "almost nineteen".'

Blaine stopped chewing and stared at him. 'Eh?'

Jake sipped his coffee and stared back imperturbably.

Sir Harry laid his fork down. 'Now see here, Sothern. I'm hanged if I'll stand for this! Call me out, by all means. Insult me if you choose. But, by

27

God, if you mean to disturb a plain man's morning head with your damned riddles...'

'Steady, steady,' Jake admonished him. 'You'll go off in an apoplexy one of these days.'

'By God, if you don't——'

Jake threw up a hand. 'Very well, very well. I'll tell you in plain words. Does the name Clem Henlow convey anything to you?'

'Henlow? Henlow? No, can't say it does.' Blaine shook his head and resumed his meal.

'No? Then try Bow Street?'

Sir Harry gaped. *'Bow Street?'*

'Bow Street,' Jake repeated.

'Good God!' Sir Harry smote his forehead. 'Of course! Bow Street. It all comes back to me. Young scoundrel tried to rob us.'

Jake sighed heavily, and leaned back in his chair. 'Harry, you are not only a hog, you are also a fool. What is worse, you put me in an extremely awkward situation. I have had to lie in my teeth to contradict your uncannily accurate description with an invented one of my own. Fortunately the worthy gentlemen of Bow Street had noted your condition. I forgive you only because you've accidentally shed some light on Clementina's mystery.'

'Who is Clementina?' demanded Sir Harry, ignoring these strictures.

'Clementina is the "young scoundrel" you went to Bow Street to complain of last night.'

Sir Harry's jaw dropped. 'A *female*? By God, Jake, I must have been badly foxed.'

'You were.'

Sir Harry frowned. 'Do you mean to tell me you knew that when you took him in—*her*, I mean, blast it!'

Jake nodded. 'Certainly. It was why I took her in.'

'You sly devil!' Blaine burst out laughing. 'Was she worth it?'

The good humour left Sothern's face suddenly. His eyes narrowed. His voice held a hint of steel. 'It wasn't like that.'

'Why not? It usually is with you. "Jake the Rake", the ladies call you. And not without reason. Not like you to miss an opportunity.'

Jake rose abruptly. He went to the window and stood looking out. Blaine's words stung. It was true. His reputation had been fairly earned. It was a reasonable assumption that he would take easy advantage of a ripe plum falling into his lap as Clementina had done. Why he had passed it up was a question he had not paused to consider until this moment. For some unaccountable reason this girl was taboo.

No. Ridiculous, he told himself. She was a child. Genteel, innocent and vulnerable in her dangerous escapade. Only a monster would have taken advantage of her situation. He might be a rake, but he played the game fairly. Never had he taken any woman against her will. He smiled inwardly, a trifle rueful. There had been no need. Until Clementina's devastatingly frank comment on his advancing years he had never encountered any woman who had shown the least aversion to him. Though no doubt he had as many defects as the next man. But he was no fool. He knew that he was one of the fortunate few who possessed a certain indefinable something that seemed to attract the opposite sex in spite of any imperfections of face or form. It had apparently failed, however, where Clementina was concerned. Perhaps he really was getting old.

A familiar figure coming down the street caught his attention. He turned back to Blaine. 'Here comes Theo. Let us see how his memory serves him.'

Evidently Theodore Farleigh's memory served him very well. Recalling all the events of the previous evening, he had repaired early to Lord Sothern's house, and what he had learned there from the porter had sent him hotfoot to Half Moon Street to seek out Sir Harry Blaine.

'For I knew it must have been you, Harry, who reported the matter to Bow Street. For I had not, and I was damned sure Sothern could not have done so.'

'You are perfectly right, Theo,' Jake assured him. 'And the fugitive from justice is even now fast asleep in bed in my grandmother's house.'

Clementina was, in fact, sitting up in a large four-poster bed with its curtains drawn back, consuming bread and butter and tea from a tray on her knees, and gazing wide-eyed at the array of gowns and petticoats Lady Staplegrove was sifting through with the aid of her dresser and the mantua-maker who had brought them all at her ladyship's bidding.

'You see, Murray, I was right about the hair,' declared her ladyship, holding up a muslin half-dress in pale green. 'Just that hint of red. This will do very well.'

'Quite right, madam,' agreed Miss Murray primly.

She was a rather sour-faced, thin creature who nevertheless had a good heart. She had herself brought up the hot milk to the young lady, and had not only warmed the sheets in the spare room, but had also personally undressed her and tucked her up in bed.

The dressmaker was nodding in vigorous agreement. '*Mais oui, madame.* You have an eye, *bien sûr.*'

The dowager came to the bed, and held the dress against Clementina. 'There. What did I tell you?'

'*Parfait!*' declared the dressmaker.

'Come on, child. Finish that tea and get up quickly so that we may try it on.'

'B-but, ma'am, I cannot possibly accept clothes from you,' Clementina protested.

'You do not mean to go about in my nightgown, I hope?' Lady Staplegrove remarked, lifting her brows.

Miss Murray tittered behind her hand, and tutted indulgently as the young lady looked nonplussed.

'N-no, but——'

'Well, then?'

'Yes, but I mean—all this!' Clementina's hand swept an arc across the clothes laid about all over the room.

'You are not going to have them all, silly child. Not that I would grudge them to you, but several would not suit. Besides, I was unsure of the size. Madame Alouette was obliged to bring a selection.'

'All of the best for *une si belle mademoiselle*,' murmured Madame Alouette.

Clementina hardly heard her. Agitatedly she seized the dowager's hand. 'Ma'am, I cannot possibly have you go to such expense on my behalf. If you will perhaps *lend* me the money to buy *one* gown, then I will——'

Lady Staplegrove shook the hand grasping hers. 'Don't be a goose, Clementina. One gown, indeed! I never heard such nonsense. Do you not see that I am enjoying myself hugely? Now don't, don't, I implore you, deny me the pleasure of dressing up a pretty young thing once again. It is no fun at all buying clothes at my age. And I do so love these new wispy little muslins, don't you? So much more comfortable than the stiff brocades we had to wear when I was a girl. What a pity they will not do for me!'

In the face of her ladyship's enthusiasm Clementina was left with nothing to say. Meekly, she rose and spent an agreeable hour being bundled in and out of the most fashionable clothes she had ever worn. There were several gowns of delicate muslin or French lawn, sprigged or spotted, and made up in styles so exquisitely cut that they emphasised all the more feminine aspects of the body. There were overgowns and petticoats, and bodices trimmed with ribbons and braid, beads and tassels, straw and feathers, spangles and foils.

A bemused Clementina found herself the possessor of a number of morning dresses, walking

dresses and evening gowns and, the provident
Madame Alouette having had the forethought to
remember outdoors wear, a pelisse and an evening
cloak were added to the collection.

Then she learned that Murray had already been
on an expedition to bring back bonnets and shoes
for her to try, together with garments of a more
intimate nature.

'For the rest,' said her ladyship airily, 'you may
borrow from my wardrobe for the present. Murray
shall find you gloves and shawls and so forth to
suit the ensembles we have chosen.'

'Oh, yes, miss,' corroborated the dresser. 'You
need not fear to go out *underdone*, as it were. We
may furnish anything, I dare say, from brooches
and pins to fans and parasols.'

Clementina could only gaze at them both, every
effort to proffer thanks being turned off with a
'Tush, my love, don't be so foolish!' from her kind
benefactress.

By the time a servant knocked on the door to
announce that Lord Sothern was downstairs
Clementina was standing before the mirror in a
charming, high-waisted muslin dress trimmed with
straw and little rosettes, over a petticoat of pale
yellow. Her short gold-red curls had been coaxed
into a more feminine style, with tendrils creeping
on to her face, emphasising its piquancy.

Lady Staplegrove draped a fine shawl culled from
her own collection across her protégée's elbow, and
declared herself satisfied.

Jake was standing frowning into the middle distance when her ladyship led Clementina into the

elegantly appointed green saloon. He turned as the
door opened and stopped short, staring.

'Aha!' uttered his grandmother triumphantly. 'I
knew you would be surprised. She is delightful, is
she not, Sothern?'

His eyes still on Clementina, the Earl moved towards them. He took Clementina's outstretched
hand, and lifted it to his lips. 'Delightful indeed.'

Clementina blushed. She was for the moment in-
capable of speech. Lord Sothern, for all his advanced years, was disturbingly attractive in the
bright light of day. Much more attractive than she
had supposed last night, with dark eyes set in a
lean-featured face, framed by dark hair which he
wore fashionably cropped. His excellent figure was
set off to admiration by the current mode for tight
buckskins and topboots, and a green cut-away
tailcoat that seemed moulded to his form.

He lifted that single eyebrow in a questioning
look, and the smile dawned. Clementina remembered the smile. It was singularly charming.

'So silent, Clementina?' he said softly. 'You had
plenty to say last night.'

Her chin came up. 'Last night you were—you behaved——'

'Abominably? Rudely?'

'Yes, both of those,' she said frankly.

'And today you find I can be quite pleasant. Even
polite. But then, last night I had to deal with a
schoolboy. Today is a very different matter. Is it
not, Miss Clementina Henlow...late of The Lawns,
near Rye in Sussex, where dwells, if memory serves
me, one Major Henlow, retired?'

Clementina paled, taking an involuntary step backwards.

'Gracious heaven, Sothern, you *have* been busy!' remarked Lady Staplegrove. 'How in the world did you glean all that information so quickly?'

Lord Sothern briefly glanced at her. 'Almost by chance, ma'am. And the instrumentality of Harry.'

'What, Blaine? How comes he into the picture, pray?'

'Oh, he was with me last night when Clementina bumped into us. Theo, too. Did I not tell you?'

'If you did I don't recall it,' Lady Staplegrove said, and then noticed Clementina's strained silence. 'Oh, my dear, how very unfortunate! Your secret is out. I am so sorry. I do so love a mystery.'

Jake came up to Clementina again, and took her hand. 'Clementina . . .'

She snatched her hand away, and stared up at him, eyes defiant in a white face.

'Well, sir? Now that you have found me out I suppose you mean to send me back.'

A rueful gleam came into his eyes. 'Certainly not. I shall have to take you back personally, otherwise you would almost certainly run away.'

'Yes, I should. Is that what you mean to do?'

The Earl studied her. 'I'm not sure. It rather depends on you.'

Clementina turned away from him, took a few agitated steps about the room, and then turned back. 'You expect me to tell you everything, is that it? Then you may judge of my actions, and make your decision accordingly.'

'She is extraordinarily acute, Sothern, you must admit,' interpolated Lady Staplegrove. 'But of course you can do nothing of the kind. You have no choice. Neither you nor I have the right to keep her from her guardians.'

'That is as may be, ma'am,' Jake responded, 'but I would rather know the circumstances so that——'

'So that you may try to order my life as they have done,' Clementina finished for him. 'Well, you won't do it. I shall tell you nothing. Except that I am not Clementina Henlow, and I am not related to Major Henlow in the very least.'

'But you did run away from his home?' Jake enquired.

'Yes. But that is the only correct information you have. And, what is more, I should like to know how you came by it.'

Jake raised an eyebrow. 'Certainly. There is no secret about that. My informant was a Bow Street Runner.'

Clementina gasped, and Lady Staplegrove uttered a shriek.

'Oh, no,' Clementina whispered. 'Oh, no.' Her legs felt weak. She looked about for the nearest chair. Seeing one by the wall behind her, she sank into it.

'Jake, how could you?' her ladyship scolded. 'Poor, dear child. Wait, I will fetch my smelling-salts.' She hurried from the room, the taffeta of her old-fashioned chemise gown rustling about her.

A couple of swift strides brought Lord Sothern to Clementina's chair, and he knelt beside her, taking her trembling hands and holding them in a comforting clasp.

'I'm sorry, my child. That was thoughtlessly cruel. Come, don't fall into a faint. It is not as bad as all that.'

Clementina raised her eyes to his. There was desperation in them and in her voice when she spoke.

'I had not thought he would go to such lengths. I guessed he might look for me himself, follow me even. But to put the Runners on to me. As though I had been a criminal!' Pulling her hands free, she rose suddenly, and began to pace about the large room, clasping and unclasping her fingers. 'This proves how right I was to run away. He does not care about me in the least. It was all false, all pretence. And to think I was willing to do as he wished! I thought it would have been the best thing for me, as he said. But it was not my welfare he cared for at all. No. Nor poor Jeremy's neither. I see it all now, clear enough. Well, he will be taken at fault. I shall not do it. And I shall see to it that he does not get Dunhythe!'

She stood silent then, breathing hard, her eyes gazing at some picture in her own mind.

Lord Sothern had said nothing through this tirade, making no attempt either to interrupt or to stop her restless pacing about the room. He stood by and watched, hoping perhaps that Clementina's passion would induce her to spill out her story. As it chanced he got little by it, but one thing he did know. He was not going to hand Clementina back to the man whose purpose she evidently feared, right or no right.

Lady Staplegrove came bustling back into the room at this moment, armed with a bottle of aromatic vinegar.

Sothern held up a hand. 'It's all right, Grandmama. She has no need of smelling-salts.'

He moved to where Clementina stood like a frozen statue, and touched her arm. The girl's head jerked round. She stared unseeingly for an instant. Then she blinked and shook her head slightly as if to clear it.

'I am sorry. I—I did not mean to make a scene.'

Jake smiled. 'You appear to have reason. Come. Sit down and let us discuss the matter calmly.'

'There is nothing to discuss,' she said, a little wearily. But she sat down on the sofa to which he led her. He remained standing, but stayed close.

Lady Staplegrove laid down her vinaigrette, and came over to sit on her other side. 'There is, on the contrary, a great deal to be discussed, my dear child. I am consumed with curiosity, and I cannot rest until I know why this Major Henlow should have sent the Runners after you. Unless of course you are really a maid and have made off with the silver or some such thing?'

'Grandmama, do you mind?' Jake protested.

'Well, it is possible. Though an adventuress would be better. I know. You meant to marry him, but decided instead to help yourself to his gold. And who shall blame you?'

'If, ma'am, you would confine your romantical notions to the novels you are so fond of reading,' Jake said acidly, 'we should do very much better.'

'Oh, tush, Sothern! I was only trying to divert her. Dear Clementina, you shall tell us nothing at all if you don't wish to.' She put out a hand and patted the girl's arm. 'And don't fret. You may stay here with me for as long as you wish. Or at least until you have decided what you would wish to do.'

'Grandmama——'

'No, Sothern, I will not hear a word. I know it is our duty to restore Clementina as soon as may be, but I, for one, have no intention of doing my duty towards a man who calls out the Bow Street Runners after a mere child.'

The Earl grinned. 'I might have guessed. Well said, Grandmama. I am in full agreement with you.'

Clementina gazed from one to the other, new hope dawning in her eyes. 'You mean you will not force me to go back? Even if I tell you nothing?'

'Gracious heaven, don't dare say a word!' exclaimed the dowager. 'You would utterly spoil everything, just when I am settling down to puzzle out the story.'

Jake groaned. 'Grandmama, would you be serious for just one moment?'

'But I am perfectly serious! If only you will eke out the clues, Clementina, I may be amused for hours guessing at your purpose.'

Clementina's lips twitched, and a chuckle escaped her. 'Oh, ma'am!'

Lady Staplegrove leaned forward and patted her hand. 'There, that is better. You see, you have nothing at all to worry about.' She glanced at the large gilt clock on the mantelshelf. 'Dear me, only look at the time! I have an engagement, and I am going to be late.' She got up. 'I must go, my dear, but what is to be done? I cannot leave Sothern with you. It would be quite irregular. But then who is to entertain you?'

Jake bowed. 'Have no fear, ma'am. In this instance I am to be trusted to behave with all the propriety in the world.'

His grandmother snorted. 'Do you think I don't know that? However, since your purpose in bringing her to me was to prevent any scandal attaching to Clementina, it must be an object with us to avoid giving the tattlemongers any food for gossip.'

'Oh, indeed,' agreed his lordship, moving to open the door for her. 'But who is to see us here, Grandmama?'

'Use your head, Sothern, do. From whose mouths but those of servants do you suppose the tabbies cull their choicest morsels? No, it will not do.'

'Very well, ma'am. Perhaps Clementina would care to drive out with me instead?'

He glanced at Clementina as he spoke, and smiled at her startled expression. 'Or do you not care for driving?'

'Oh, yes, but——'

'An excellent suggestion,' chimed in the dowager. 'No one could object to that. It is quite in the mode to be seen in the park with a gentleman. A groom up behind, too.'

She bustled over to her charge, pulled her up from the sofa, and began to push her towards the door.

'What a pity we did not keep the cherry riding habit, though to be sure it became you not. Still, you may wear the sprigged walking dress and the blue pelisse. Murray shall lend you my chinchilla muff, and——'

'But, ma'am, I cannot,' Clementina cried, breaking in on these cheerful plans before Lady Staplegrove had quite managed to thrust her from the room. 'I mean, it wouldn't be—I am not here to——'

'Oh, tush, child! What a piece of work you make of a very small matter!' The dowager turned to her grandson. 'Persuade her, dear boy. I positively *must* go.'

She opened the door and whisked from the room, only to pop her head in again a second later.

'Shall we see you at Maria Spencer's musical soirée this evening? A very dull affair, with a number of talentless performers, I gather, but what would you? One must be seen.'

'I shall be devastated to miss it, of course,' said Jake satirically, 'but I am otherwise engaged.'

He reddened very slightly on the words, and his grandmother's keen eye sharpened.

'I see,' she said flatly.

There was a brief pause. Clementina glanced from one to the other, sensing tension. She saw Lady Staplegrove compress her lips firmly, and wondered what it was she was resolving not to say.

As if she felt the girl's scrutiny the dowager's eyes turned to Clementina, and she smiled warmly.

'Then we shall not see him there, child. Make the most, then, of your present opportunity.'

Upon which rather elliptical remark she was gone, leaving the door correctly ajar behind her.

Clementina gazed after her in some consternation.

'What did she mean, my lord? She cannot intend to take me to parties while I am here.'

'Why not?' Jake asked flippantly.

'Well, because—because she does not know me. Besides, I am not a guest in her house, but a—a——'

'A what?'

'Well, an interloper, a fugitive.'

'Oh, no. That was a Master Clem Henlow. You are Miss Clementina... Hm. We shall have to think up a name for you.'

'Oh, there is no need of that,' she said, sighing. 'You will find it out soon enough, I dare say. But you will not have heard of it. It is Hythe.'

'Very well, Miss Hythe. Let us say that your mother was an old friend of my mother's, and nothing could be more natural than for Grandmama to ask you for a visit now that you are of an age to go into Society.'

Clementina fixed him with that curiously wide gaze. 'And no one will then wonder at your taking a passing interest in one little older than a schoolgirl. Thus you will be safe from gossiping tongues.'

Taken aback, Jake blinked. 'It had not crossed my mind, but I dare say you are right.'

'I am,' Clementina averred. 'It would hardly be becoming in me to lay you open to further gossip after all your grandmother's kindness. She has as much thought for me, you notice. Besides, I am sure she could not like it. Though I doubt it would trouble you over-much.'

Jake's jaw dropped perceptibly. 'Faith, I don't know whether to be angry or to laugh!'

Clementina merely looked at him enquiringly. Laughter won. He came to her, and tilted her chin with one finger.

'You are an impertinent little minx, my dear. And you don't even know it.' He paused, aware suddenly of a pull from the guileless wide gaze tugging at his own.

'You have green eyes,' he said inconsequently, taking in the fact.

'Yes,' she answered. 'Yours are dark brown. Soulful, I think. Do they account for your success with the ladies, do you suppose?'

CHAPTER THREE

JAKE released her chin abruptly.

'If you mean to drive out with me,' he said curtly, 'you had better change your dress.'

Clementina gazed at him, brows raised in amazement. 'If this is your notion of persuasion, my lord, I no longer wonder at your successes. How could any lady possibly resist?'

The Earl stood for a moment, defiant and glaring. Then his lips twitched. Clementina's green eyes twinkled responsively.

'Dear Clementina,' Jake said, bowing with exaggerated formality, 'pray do me the honour of driving out with me.'

Clementina curtsied prettily. 'The honour is all mine, sir.'

Then they both burst into laughter. Jake took her by the shoulders and pushed her, unresisting, through the door.

'Away with you, baggage!'

Giggling, Clementina sped away. She did not keep him waiting very long, and they were soon bowling through the streets in his natty phaeton and four towards Hyde Park.

Clementina, dressed as Lady Staplegrove had directed, with the addition of a very pretty little poke bonnet trimmed with fur, was at first too interested in taking in her surroundings to have much leisure for conversation.

She had passed through the metropolis before, of course, but until now she had never penetrated into the more fashionable quarter. She could not help but be impressed with the high porticos and elegant frontages to the houses they passed. Indeed, even Lady Staplegrove's rather modest house in Brook Street had, by the new light of day, seemed imposing to one more used to the less impressive residences of Norwich, the closest large town to her old home of Dunhythe.

She said as much aloud, quite forgetting her determination to keep her origins to herself. Foolishly perhaps, Jake alerted her to her own indiscretion.

'So, Miss Hythe of Dunhythe, your home is in Norfolk.'

Clementina looked round quickly, meeting his amused gaze with dismay in her own eyes.

'Don't be concerned, my child,' the Earl said soothingly. 'You have given nothing away. Dunhythe you had already mentioned. I dare say I might pursue enquiries in Norfolk and come up with various answers. But I surmise that, your flight being from Rye, Norfolk has very little to do with it. Though you were headed that way, were you not?'

Clementina bit her lip, eyeing him uncertainly.

'Your grandmama told me I might keep my own counsel,' she began slowly. 'Yet you insist on trying to trip me into saying more.'

'Grandmama is more complacent than I,' he revealed, one eyebrow lifting as his lips curved into a teasing smile. 'Besides, you intrigue me...more every second.'

The dark eyes held hers a moment longer, their expression disturbing. Clementina felt an intimacy in that look, a warmth which left her a little breathless. As he turned his attention back to his horses she became aware of the quickening of her heartbeat. To cover it she broke into stuttering speech.

'Well, y-you are scarcely to be com-commended on your own frankness, sir. After all, beyond your name and the identity of your grandmother I know—I know very little about you, either.'

'Oh, I have no secrets, ma'am,' laughed Jake. 'For which the town tabbies will vouch, believe me.'

'I don't mean gossip,' Clementina uttered crossly, rapidly regaining her composure. 'Lord, sir, I am not such a simpleton as to believe the half of the stories that have reached us, even in my rural fastness!' She turned to him with that wide innocence in her gaze. 'But I know nothing else of you, my lord.'

Jake's lip curled. Yet he spoke lightly. 'What is there to know? My history is as tedious as the next man's born to a title and lands. One learns to manage the estates, to do the pretty to the same faces over and over again. One sports and gambles, one dances and flirts. One marries at length and begets an heir to pursue the same game once more. Fascinating, is it not?'

He turned his head as he spoke, and encountered an odd look in his companion's eye. He let out an involuntary laugh.

'But what have I said to make you look at me so?'

'Nothing,' Clementina answered quickly, turning away. 'I don't know how I looked.'

'Compassionate,' he informed her at once. 'You pity me, perhaps? I wonder why. Surely I am to be envied?'

'I don't think so,' Clementina said quietly. 'You are plainly bored to death. Small wonder you kick up a riot and rumpus at every chance!'

Jake burst out laughing. 'I wish Grandmama could hear you. "A riot and rumpus". Hark at the pot! I dare swear not one of my exploits would bring down as much trouble on me as yours is like to do.'

'That is easily remedied,' Clementina snapped. 'It was not I who insisted on staying with Lady Staplegrove.'

'Softly, child,' his lordship warned, jerking his head backwards to remind her of the presence of his groom clinging to his perch behind.

Clementina flushed and looked away.

There was enough to take her interest. They were driving down Piccadilly, and the press of carriages was intense. Spanking new chariots with crests on their panels jostled for space with lumbering coaches of a bygone era now turned to the use of a hackney. The Bath stagecoach clattered by as the Earl's team picked its way through a maze of smaller vehicles—whiskies and drays, carts and horsemen. Darting in between and passing down the pavements either side went artisans with their tools in hand, sweeps with blackened faces and a collection of brushes on their backs, street vendors with their trays of wares, servants in livery, and all manner of people going about their legitimate business.

But the bustle had little power to hold Clementina's attention, which was concentrated on the need to mind her tongue. In an effort to distract Sothern from further questions she asked one of her own.

'Are you as fortunate in all your relatives as with your grandmother?'

Jake laughed. 'By no means. Most have long since despaired of me. But Grandmama is...special to me. She more or less brought me up, you see.'

Clementina turned interested eyes to examine his profile. 'How was that?'

'My mother—Grandmama's daughter, you understand—died when I was a mere boy. When my father remarried, Grandmama did not approve his choice.' He turned his head, grinning. 'I believe she kicked up a good deal of "riot and rumpus".'

'I can well imagine it,' Clementina said, smiling at this sally. 'Did she take you to live with her?'

'Not exactly. But I spent most of my holidays from school with her and my grandfather. And if she did not quite stand to me in place of a mother she certainly bore more of the burden than anyone else.'

'And your stepmother? Did she not care for you?'

The Earl gave a short laugh. 'She had no time. She bred like a rabbit, poor woman.'

'Have you then a numerous family?' Clementina asked, conscious of a pang of envy.

'No, for only three of her offspring survived infancy. They were among the last of her brood, and consequently not of an age to lend me companionship. Indeed, the eldest of them must be some years your junior. Fifteen or sixteen, I should imagine.'

'You mean you don't know?' Clementina exclaimed, shocked.

Sothern shrugged. 'Why should I? I am barely acquainted with them. On my father's death Caroline retired with her children to the Dower House, and has remained there to this day.'

'Do you never visit her?' she asked wonderingly.

'Certainly. I make a point of it whenever I am on the estate. To tell the truth, I believe it is as much a penance for Caroline as for myself. She is excessively indolent, you know, and abhors any form of exertion. Or perhaps she is merely exhausted from the rigours of child-bearing.'

'I should not be surprised,' Clementina agreed. 'I had an aunt who was of the same type. *None* of her children survived. She died with the last.'

'And so you have no close family, either?'

'Not on my mother's side. But on Papa's there is——'

Clementina broke off. Her hand slipped from her muff and was brought up to touch her fingers to her lips as if to prevent any more words from emerging. Under the poke of her bonnet the green eyes glowered at Jake.

'Very clever, my lord!'

His lordship grinned and raised an eyebrow. 'But not clever enough for Miss Hythe, I take it?'

'Certainly not,' she averred crossly, 'if you think to lull me into chattering about my circumstances.'

He sighed and murmured softly so that his groom should not hear, 'I wish you could find it in you to trust me.'

Clementina looked away, down into her lap where her agitated fingers began aimlessly to play with the muff, plucking at the fur and stroking it.

'It—it is not that I mistrust you, sir,' she said, low-voiced and gruff.

'Then I wish you will confide in me, my child.'

'I *cannot*,' she replied in a stifled voice.

He was silent.

Clementina sat fighting an irrational impulse to apologise for her reticence. She owed him no explanations, for although he had been kind he had interfered in an extremely high-handed manner. Who knew but what he might, if he knew all, bring her escapade to a summary end? Besides, she could not bring herself to tell him—nor *anyone* indeed!—of the preposterous proposals that had driven her into flight. Who would believe it? She was scarcely able herself to believe that anyone could expect a girl of quality to lend herself to such a scheme. Sothern must suppose her to have invented the whole thing, even could she force her tongue to relate to him what had so filled her with disgust and horror.

She drew a somewhat ragged breath and sat up straighter, forcing her thoughts away from the memories and out to the world about her. She became aware that the horses had slowed to a walk, and they were entering the park through an open pair of massive wrought-iron gates. Lord Sothern picked his horses up to a gentle trot as he turned the phaeton into the carriageway that led around the park, and Clementina had leisure to look about her.

Hyde Park was laid out in a picturesque way, the rides bordered by elegant trees with acres of undulating greensward leading down to the Serpentine. There was quite a number of riders in pairs or groups, and several vehicles making their leisurely way towards the main thoroughfare where the beau monde was wont to parade in the afternoon. At this hour it would not be as crowded, the Earl reflected, for the fashionable morning promenade took place rather on foot, down the Queens Walk along the shore of the reservoir in Green Park.

But it proved quite sufficiently so for Clementina. Within a very few minutes it was borne in on her how imprudent she had been to come out on this drive.

'Gracious, how they stare!' she ejaculated, as she encountered what must have been the fourth or fifth look of blatant curiosity on the face of a matron who rode with another in an open carriage.

'Pay no attention,' Jake advised, merely bowing at the lady as they passed by.

'It's very well for you,' Clementina retorted, thoroughly agitated. 'You are used to it.' She cast him a resentful glance. 'And I dare say if I was not with you they would not notice me at all. How foolish of me not to have foreseen how it would be! It was foolish of you, too. More so.'

'Let me tell you, my girl, there are many who would give their eye-teeth to be where you are now!' Jake flung at her, stung.

'The more fool they!'

'Why, you little——'

'Careful,' Clementina whispered fiercely, throwing in her turn a significant glance behind her.

Jake closed his lips, but threw her a fiery look that boded her little good presently. But he was disarmed in a moment or two when Clementina spoke again, a catch in her voice.

'P-please, my lord, take me back. I-I cannot *bear* this.'

He glanced down and saw tears standing in the green eyes. His heart melted, and he reached one hand across to clasp hers where they lay tightly gripped in her lap over the discarded muff.

'Don't mind it, sweetheart. I'll take you home.'

Only when she was safely back in Lady Staplegrove's comforting pink parlour did Clementina remember that he had used that tender endearment.

No, he could not have said it, she thought, a tingle in her veins. He could not have! She was mistaken, surely. She must have misheard him.

But his voice echoed in her mind. *'Don't mind it, sweetheart'.*

* * *

The Earl was not even aware of what he had said. He had been conscious only that this young girl, whom he had voluntarily taken in charge, had been caused distress. It had indeed been thoughtless of him so to expose her to the avid curiosity of the world. She had been right. It was because she was with him that she had attracted attention.

Normally he would have laughed it off, cynically imagining the speculative whisperings of his numerous acquaintance. Now, for the first time, he was conscious of remorse. None knew better than he how damaging such talk could be. It was unforgivable to have put the child in such a situation.

He could think of nothing else all day. Meeting his friends at their club did not help. He found Blaine and Theodore Farleigh at Brooks, partaking of refreshment and perusing the papers in a quiet corner of one of the small saloons, out of the way of the hardened gamesters already at play in the Great Subscription Room.

'Whole town's talking again, old fellow,' Sir Harry Blaine told him, waving his half-empty tankard for emphasis. 'Can't count the number of fools who have asked me who is your latest flirt.'

'Hell and damnation!' swore his lordship in a savage undervoice.

'You may well curse,' pronounced Mr Farleigh gloomily. 'Had you at least had sense enough to introduce her here and there you might have avoided the worst of it.'

Jake's eyes turned to him, swift suspicion kindling. 'You are not going to tell me people are stupid enough to think——'

'Ha! And he calls me fool!' There was a note of triumph in Sir Harry's voice. But he lowered his tone as Farleigh urgently counselled him to, '*Hush*, for pity's sake! Do you want the whole room to hear?'

'What else are they to think, hey?' Sir Harry pursued. 'A man may flaunt his mistress in public. He don't come smash up to the matrons and give them her hand to shake. No, by God! Ruined, that's what she is. Ruined.'

Appalled, the Earl could only gaze at him.

'Don't heed him, Jake,' Theo uttered quietly, grasping his friend's arm and giving it a reassuring squeeze. 'People may think what they like, but this coil may soon be mended, trust me.'

'How?' demanded Jake hoarsely. 'How?'

'Your grandmother, old fellow. She'll scotch it fast enough. Let 'em see she sponsors the girl, and all will be well. They'll learn their error fast enough.'

'Yes, by God! See to it, man,' ordered Blaine with a lightning change of face. 'See to it on the instant.'

Jake was staring at Theo, some of the horror leaving his drawn features.

'You may be right, Theo. Yes, you are right. She is planning to do so this very evening, in fact. The Spencer woman has some musical event planned, and my grandmother means to take Clementina there.'

'Excellent! That will do finely.'

'Sensible woman, Lady Staplegrove,' said Blaine enthusiastically, adding his mite. 'She'll see all's right.'

But it seemed at first as though his friends were mistaken. Jake was engaged for the evening with his mistress, but so anxious was he to see his folly righted that he sent a note excusing himself, and set out instead for the projected musical soirée.

Such was his state of mind that it did not even occur to him that Lady Matilda might also have heard the gossip, and that his breaking of their engagement might have been expressly designed to lend colour to the rumours so gleefully spilled into her ears.

But Lord Sothern was doomed to disappointment. He had no difficulty entering the house of Mrs Maria Spencer, a notable hostess, for he had not actually refused her invitation, it being his invariable careless practice to leave most cards of invitation unanswered.

Having greeted his hostess, he passed through into the saloon behind her. The rooms were jammed with members of the beau monde, most of whom had little or no musical appreciation, but came mainly for the pleasure of greeting their acquaintance and being seen. For Mrs Spencer's parties were always in vogue, and anyone who aspired to a place in the fashionable set must necessarily flaunt their eligibility to receive one of her exclusive invitations.

From one of the four interconnecting rooms, each decorated in striped brocade wall-hangings of a different hue, floated the rather reedy fluting of a tenor voice, rendering an operatic aria in the Italian tongue. A grimace of distaste flitted across the Earl's features as his eyes searched the throng for a sight of his grandmother and Clementina.

'Why, Sothern,' a female voice hailed him, 'what a pleasant surprise! I little thought to see you at such an affair as this.'

The Earl turned to greet Lady Waldemar, a handsome matron of middle years, on whose excellent figure the current fashion for high waists looked very well. She was a close friend of his grandmother.

'Why, no, ma'am,' he replied, a satirical smile on his lips. 'I am not often to be found present on these occasions. But my grandmother assured me of the superiority of the performers, and I did not dare to absent myself for fear of missing such delights as this presently afforded.' He waved an arm in the direction of the warbling tenor.

Lady Waldemar's eyes twinkled. 'Indeed, yes. A most moving performance.'

His eyebrow went up. 'So I perceive. It has moved you quite out of the room!'

Betrayed into a laugh, her ladyship shut her fan and dealt him a rap over the knuckles.

'Dreadful boy!'

Sothern smiled. 'Have you seen Grandmama, by the by?'

'Certainly. You will find her in the room *opposite* our tuneful friend in there.'

He was tempted to ask after Clementina, and thought it odd that Lady Waldemar should not have mentioned her. But he bowed, and was about to pass on with a word of thanks when she touched his arm to stay him.

'I expect you at my rout, mind.' The twinkle reappeared. 'After your appearance here tonight I shall brook no excuses.'

'I shall try not to disappoint you, ma'am.'

He moved away on the words, reflecting that at least one person appeared not to have heard the gossip. But it very quickly became obvious that Lady Waldemar was either too tactful or too fond of his grandmother to distress her by mentioning the matter. For as the Earl made his way through the room he was obliged to greet a number of acquaintances. Though none had the temerity to ask embarrassing questions there were several eyes that spoke teasing messages at variance with the conventional innocence of their actual words. Then, when he located his grandmother at last, it was only to find that she had come alone.

'What?' he ejaculated in an urgent undervoice, guiding her quickly aside to an alcove where they might speak without being overheard. 'She is not here? How is this? I made sure you would bring her.'

'It is no use blaming me, Sothern. She would not come. Heaven knows I cannot blame her after what she was obliged to endure today!'

'Oh, *Grandmama*. All my dependence was on you. You have no idea of the tongues I have set wagging this day.'

'Have I not, indeed? I have been quite adequately informed, I thank you.'

'By Lady Waldemar, perhaps?'

'Among others.'

'I thought as much.'

'Yes, but at least Hetty had the goodness to tell me what was toward. The others merely took delight in twitting me on your latest fall from grace.'

The Earl groaned. 'Faith, I have made wretched work of it! Now what is to be done?'

Lady Staplegrove relented. 'Don't put yourself about. I am as much to blame as you, remember. I should have foreseen the consequences of that rash outing. Never fear. I shall take Clementina about with me tomorrow and settle the matter.'

Jake was frowning heavily. 'I hope you may be able to do so.'

'Oh tush, nothing could be easier! I am well able to handle the tabbies.'

'I don't doubt it, ma'am. Nor your ability to persuade Clementina to acquiesce... *if* she is still with you.'

The dowager raised startled brows. 'You do not suppose that she will run off again?'

'She may already have done so. Certainly flight might well have seemed preferable to running the gamut of the beau monde once more. And what could be simpler for her with neither of us at hand?'

His grandmother grasped his wrist. 'Well, don't stand dithering, man! Go and see. I will follow and——'

'No. If we both leave it will occasion remark. You can do more good here, ma'am. A few words in the right ears, and we will soon give the world to understand that Clementina is an eminently

respectable visitor whom you are about to introduce into Society.'

'And much good that will do if she is already
gone,' said the dowager acidly. 'For the Lord's sake
send me word!'

'If she has gone I will do so. If you do not hear
from me you will know that she is safe in Brook
Street.'

But the conviction that Clementina had indeed
run away again grew upon him as he swiftly walked
the few short streets from Mrs Spencer's residence
in Park Street to his grandmother's house. He
wondered how he would set about finding her
again. It did not so much as cross his mind that he
might wash his hands of her and leave her to fend
for herself. She had blundered into his life by
accident, but even in this short time he had come
to feel himself responsible for her. At least until he
saw her safe in other hands. Hands, moreover, that
he could be certain would care for her welfare with
the respect and concern that was her due.

There were one or two clues, of course.
Dunhythe, her home in Norfolk. She had confessed that that was her original destination. She
would scarcely alter that plan. Unless there were
other relatives to whom she might flee. What had
she said? None on her mother's side. Too bad she
had recollected herself before giving out any information on her paternal relations. Still, if she had
gone he did not doubt his ability to catch her up
soon enough. Unless, that is, some other and less
scrupulous person were to cross her path before he
had a chance to do so.

This thought sent him on at a speedier pace, heart beating faster as his reluctant mind drew for him sundry graphic pictures of the fate that might so easily overtake a young girl on her own.

Answering the door to his lordship's peremptory knock, Lady Staplegrove's butler found himself the recipient of a pithy confidence as he was brushed aside by the Earl's hand.

'A fine mess we may be in now, Dorridge, and no mistake! If only Miss Clementina has not given you all the slip.'

He was hurrying to the stairs as he spoke, and had begun to mount them two at a time, evidently with the idea of checking Clementina's bed-chamber. He was brought up short by the butler's call.

'My lord! My lord! If, as I apprehend, you are looking for the young lady, she is certainly here. I can vouch for that.'

'I'll see for myself, I thank you,' the Earl said, on the move again.

'But Miss Clementina is down here, my lord,' pursued Dorridge, following him up a step or two. 'In the pink parlour.'

Sothern turned and quickly came back down the stairs. Arrived at the door of the parlour, he flung it wide, and strode into the room, stopping short at the sight that met his eyes.

A meagre pink light glancing off the furnishings was afforded by the two small branches of cande-labra on the mantelpiece. In this warm setting Clementina sat, curled up before the hearth, clad in an over-large dressing-gown which had slipped from its place about her neck to expose one slim shoulder to the blaze. Shadows flickered across her face and hair, and the firelight touched that bare expanse of flesh to glimmering gold.

Never in his life had Jake beheld so desirable an object.

CHAPTER FOUR

CLEMENTINA raised startled eyes to meet those of the Earl. He stood stock still, dumbfounded by the picture she presented.

'My l-lord,' she faltered.

'You *are* here,' he uttered stupidly. 'I thought— I was certain...'

His voice died. Assailed by a riot of chaotic emotions, he was unable even to think, much less speak. Her beauty was delicate, but there was a sensuality about her. She was a child, an urchin, and still all woman. Her pose was unconsciously inviting, yet touchingly vulnerable.

Jake was confused, for under the fierce pulsing of his blood, a feeling he well recognised, was one wholly unfamiliar. A bewildering, but nevertheless violent urge to snatch her up in his arms and cradle her to his chest, there to hold her safe forever.

As if she sensed his desire Clementina's fingers came up to tug at the fallen edge of her neckline, concealing the glowing warmth of her skin.

'Don't,' Jake uttered involuntarily, stepping forward a pace and throwing out a hand.

Clementina jerked back. The Earl retreated.

'I beg your pardon. It is just that—I mean...' He gave a self-conscious laugh. 'You look so charmingly. Don't spoil it.'

Biting her lip, Clementina hugged the dressing-gown closer about her shoulders.

'You should not be here,' she said in a gruff tone meant to hide her confusion.

'I know. I won't remain above a moment.'

He hesitated, uncertain what to say, what to do, knowing only that he could not bring himself to leave. Not yet.

'May I sit down?' he asked at length, adding quickly, 'But I have no wish to disturb you.'

The tone and the words were so unlike his usual manner that Clementina felt strangely uncomfortable. More disturbing still was the expression in his eyes as they ran over her, never leaving her, seeming to probe even beneath the folds of the silken robe that covered her to the nakedness beneath.

She had been foolish to come downstairs thus clad, but her bedchamber had seemed cold and lonely, and she had been unable to sleep. But, when she had stolen down the stairs and into the pink parlour with only the glow of the dying embers of the fire to light it, the butler had followed her in.

Had she but known it she owed it to Dorridge that she was still here. He had been on his way to the servants' quarters when he had seen her come down. Debating within himself whether to call her ladyship's maid, who would have had no hesitation in escorting her right back upstairs, he thought of his mistress and decided against it. A lifetime of service to a lady of decidedly unconventional habits had engendered in the butler a tolerance which he knew Murray did not share. The young lady had a deal to worry her, by all he had overheard. Best to let her be.

But in a spirit of fatherly benevolence he did what he could to make her more comfortable. Without saying a word he had lit candles and made up the fire.

'A hot drink, miss?' he had then asked kindly.

'Thank you, Dorridge.' Clementina had smiled. 'Hot milk would be very welcome, if you please.'

It seemed only a few minutes later that she had heard the commotion in the hall. Then Jake had erupted in to stare at her in a way that rendered her acutely conscious of her dishabille.

'It—it is not very seemly,' she managed to say, 'for you to stay.'

'No, I know,' Jake agreed. *But I can't go.*

Only he did not say it aloud. He moved to an armchair, and leaned down to pick up a footstool. Placing it near Clementina, he sat down. She swallowed, and could not help but shift her position slightly.

'Don't draw away,' he said softly.

There was silence for a moment or two. Unable to meet the heat of his gaze, Clementina turned to look at the less threatening fire. His voice came again, still hushed, as if a louder tone might shatter the intimacy of the moment.

'I was afraid you had gone.'

'No,' she stated simply. She turned to look at him then. 'Though I did not dare to go abroad with your grandmother tonight.'

'A pity,' was his only comment.

Silence fell again.

A sense of unreality began to invade Clementina, as if she were living in a dream. Jake was so close she had only to reach out to touch him. But instinct warned that if she did so she would unleash the powerful force emanating from him. A force so strong it was almost tangible. It tugged her eyes back to meet the dark pools of his own, glittering oddly in the firelight.

'You frighten me,' Clementina whispered.

Instantly he reached out, and his fingers caressed her cheek. His voice was tender.

'You have nothing to fear from me. I will never hurt you.'

From behind them there came a discreet cough. Both looked quickly round to see the butler standing by the still open doorway, a silver tray in his hand.

'Your milk, miss,' he pronounced loudly.

The prosaic utterance dispelled the heavy atmosphere at once.

Sothern rose as Dorridge came forward to offer the glass on the salver with a dignified bow. Clementina took it with a smile and a word of thanks. Dorridge retreated to the door, and stood with his fingers on the handle, his limpid but respectful gaze resting significantly on the Earl. He was not quite so tolerant as all that, his pose seemed to suggest.

Jake took the hint, and laughed. 'Yes, very well, Dorridge. I will be leaving shortly.'

He turned to Clementina as the butler left the room, and held out a hand. His mobile eyebrow was raised quizzically.

'Come. Your admirable chaperon is perfectly right. I must go, and you should be in bed.'

He was back to his normal self. Clementina gave him her hand, and allowed him to help her to her feet.

'Thank you, my lord. Forgive my indiscretion, if you please. I know I should not have come down dressed like this.'

Jake grinned. 'For unconventionality, ma'am, I have never met your equal. I can't think how you have survived unmolested to this day!'

'My dearest child, you have no choice in the matter,' said Lady Staplegrove firmly, leaning across the discarded breakfast cups to clasp Clementina's hand.

'Dear ma'am, I beg of you not to ask it of me,' she persisted in agitation, gripping the elder woman's fingers.

'I have to, my love. Really, there is no other course open to us. We cannot leave matters as they stand.'

'But I do not see that it makes any difference what people say of me,' Clementina protested. 'I am hardly likely to make an appearance in London again, much less thrust myself into the beau monde. Indeed, I have no wish to do so.'

The dowager sighed wearily. 'I declare you are as self-willed as Sothern! And far less easy to manage, I may add.'

Clementina reddened. 'I—I am sorry, ma'am. I do not mean to be disobliging. Especially after your kindness to me.'

'Fiddlesticks!' said her ladyship, reviving. 'I want to hear no more of that, if you please. If you will not do it for yourself you may do it for Jake. He is quite devastated at having led people to imagine the worst of you. I have rarely seen him so anxious. Indeed, it is the first time I have ever known him to care what people may say.'

Clementina bit her lip. She was indebted to Lady Staplegrove for the information that her presence in Lord Sothern's phaeton had led the world to dub her a member of the *demi-monde*. She had been shocked, but also gratified that Jake himself had spared her the embarrassment of hearing it from him last night. She had been touched, too, to learn that he had dashed from the musical soirée to find her when he feared she might have run away again.

But she was still reluctant to accompany the dowager on the round of morning visits which her ladyship said would best serve to scotch the rumours.

Her ladyship was already dressed for the expedition in an open robe worn over a plain petticoat with a cross-over handkerchief tied over all. A costume which for the sake of comfort had been her customary undress wear over the last ten years. Such concessions to fashion as she made were mostly confined to collars, colours and trimmings, and a variety of rather startling large hats over her grey wig, still frizzed in the style of the eighties. She could not take to the new greatcoats and pelisses with their tight-fitting sleeves, and kept to voluminous cloaks, invariably of velvet, and richly furred for warmth.

'Ma'am,' Clementina resumed rather desperately, 'can you not see that you would be perpetrating an outrageous fraud? For all you know of me you can scarcely vouch for my respectability. Yesterday when Lord Sothern offered to take me driving I had not seriously considered the implications, or I would not have gone. Now that these rumours have arisen, surely it would be far better that I never appear again, and——'

'And make me out even more of a cheat and a fool then if you were to enter Society under *fraudulent* conditions,' Lady Staplegrove interrupted tartly. 'My dear girl, I have already paved the way. By this time my various acquaintance will have apprised each other of your presence in my house. How am I to explain to them that you are not here, after all? At the least, they will suppose me to be in my dotage, which I most certainly am not, let me tell you!'

'No, indeed you are not,' Clementina agreed with a rueful smile. 'I am behaving altogether churlishly, dear ma'am. Forgive me, pray.'

The dowager beamed. 'If that means that you have come to your senses at last, I will willingly do so.'

Clementina nodded. 'Since there is no help for it, ma'am, I suppose I must come with you.'

'Excellent. That pretty gown with the straw borders will do very well. I mean you to beat all our débutantes to flinders!'

Clementina laughed at the glee in Lady Staplegrove's voice, but it was in some trepidation that she set out with her on the projected round of visits.

They began innocuously enough. A contemporary of the dowager's, Lady Seagrave was very large, very jolly, and extremely deaf. She understood not one word in ten that was addressed to her, but since she talked almost without cessation this was hardly felt to be a serious handicap to conversation.

She inhabited a rather small house in Mount Street, which was stuffed to bursting point with the largest collection of heavy old-fashioned Queen Anne furniture that Clementina had ever seen. The rooms were consequently dark and gloomy, with heavy drapery to the windows of faded burgundy or deep purple. There was a smell of must and a degree of visible dust, too.

Only in the one parlour where the old lady received her guests was the dour atmosphere lightened. There was less furniture, and the drapes were new and of a light blue. Occupying most of one sofa by herself, Lady Seagrave sat hugely enjoying her own conversation. She never went out, and was consequently always very happy to see anyone who took the trouble to visit her.

'Very good of you to come, my dear,' she would boom, regardless of the identity of the caller. 'Can't get out, you see, these days. Indeed, can scarcely get out of the chair, let alone prance down the street! Chairs, of course, used to walk themselves in my day. Few of them about now. Besides, couldn't expect the poor fellows to bear my bulk, now could you?'

Here Lady Seagrave would laugh heartily, her several chins rippling. Then she would be off again, her discourse ranging from the difficulties her servants suffered in assisting her from one place to another—not least because of the crush of furnishings to every room—to a description of her last gargantuan meal and what was expected to be on the menu for today.

It seemed to Clementina unlikely that Lady Seagrave even took in the fact of her existence, let alone bearing any part in discussions of her status, as she candidly pointed out to her patron.

'You would be surprised, my love,' responded the dowager, as they re-entered her town chariot to be carried to the next port of call. 'She is not really as deaf as she makes out, nor as immobile. Had I been alone I have not the slightest doubt that she would not only have betrayed knowledge of you, but would have demanded the whole story. As it is, she will certainly pass on a detailed description of you, and verify the fact that you are my guest to any cronies who visit her in the next day or two.'

The next three ladies on the dowager's list were all prominent society matrons, whose far more fashionable velvet and damask-cushioned parlours were in a constant bustle of comings and goings. Here were light wood tables and sofas, shapely legs turned and twisted, often painted white or gilt. Brocades in figures or fashionable stripes to the walls and chairs, or plain-painted walls beautifully offset by figured drapes. Twinkling chandeliers, mirrors and portraits, gilt and ormolu ornaments. But the whole sparsely done, so that each item showed its merits alone to make together an elegant setting for the *bon ton* parading within.

Clementina's head whirled with names and faces, few of which she was able to match. There were, though, some names she recognised from local Norfolk gossip, together with those culled from the lips of Margery Plumstead, who had spent some years in attendance on the daughters of one family who graced the London scene before she had come to Dunhythe to supervise Clementina's own transition into a lady.

Her initial trepidation gave place to a lively interest in the people who made up this extraordinary élite. On the surface they were all silks and furbelows, perfumes and rouge, but Clementina's quick intelligence discerned the ordinary human frailties under the genteel façade, and she swiftly reached the conclusion that people were really the same no matter what their station in life. No awestruck bread and butter débutante she!

There were several such scattered among the various callers. Young girls her own age, thrust willy-nilly into the glare of public view, their attributes or shortcomings bound either for critical acclaim or rejection, their presence meant to achieve one solitary purpose: marriage.

'I cannot think,' Clementina said to Lady Staplegrove between visits in the privacy of the carriage, 'that my first appearance can be of more than passing interest to these girls, or indeed their mothers, who are only anxious to get them off as advantageously as they can in the least possible amount of time!'

'Don't be naïve, child,' came her ladyship's dry response. 'You forget that the majority of our circle is made up of those who are either safely wed—in which case their main pursuit is for enjoyment, and gossip forms the better part of that—or those who have long since abandoned pretensions to matrimony. The latter, poor souls, have nothing else to occupy them. No children of their own to concern themselves over. There is no one so ready, believe me, to blast a reputation as an ape-leader who has failed to secure a husband.'

'I can readily believe it,' Clementina uttered on a faintly bitter note. 'What else has a female to hope for? Oh, to be a man!'

Lady Staplegrove looked round quickly, peering closely at the girl's face, which she could barely see in the gloom of the carriage. Did that unguarded plea indicate that here lay the child's own concern? She was tempted to put a question, but she was far too wise for that. Already Clementina had put a hand to her mouth as if to push back the words that had inadvertently slipped out.

'I cannot agree with you,' she said instead. 'For all the disadvantages, I am persuaded we females have a much more amusing time of it.'

This led immediately to a lively argument which lasted until they arrived at their destination. Here Clementina was instantly put out of countenance by recognising the hostess as one of those who had stared her down during her drive with Sothern in the park. The matron, though gracious, proved as supercilious as her original look had promised, and

Clementina was glad when the dowager cut their visit short.

'For we positively must visit Hetty—the Lady Waldemar, you know—who will, I am sure, command me to bring you to her rout tomorrow.'

So indeed it proved. Her ladyship still resided in the family mansion in Hanover Square, the fatherless Viscount having only recently come of age, and she was obliged to maintain a level of pomp that fairly stunned a young provincial. Pages seemed to spring forward at every hand to open doors, and a very stately butler guided the ladies up a massive staircase, along apparently endless corridors, to what appeared to be a vast saloon bedecked with blue hangings, full-length gilt-framed mirrors, an enormous suite of matching sofas and chairs done out in gold and blue brocade, and peopled by a positive forest of morning callers.

It was a relief to find the mistress of this overpowering establishment as unpretentious and friendly as Lady Staplegrove herself. She smiled warmly at Clementina, and clasped her hand in both her own.

'But she is enchanting, my dear Alicia! Quite enchanting. Now, dear child, you must attend my party. I will not hear of a refusal. I have secured Sothern already, so you need not fear to be among strangers.'

'It—it is very kind of you, ma'am.'

'Nothing of the sort,' stated Lady Waldemar with a gentle laugh. 'I am doing myself a service, if you want the truth. I had not expected a large number of young persons, and had made no provision for dancing. Just a conversable evening, you know, with a few card-tables set out and a little music.'

She saw disbelief in Clementina's face, and laughed out.

'Yes, I know. It does seem as if we must always be ceremonious in such a house as this. Absurdly grand, is it not? But we contrive to make it cosy, in spite of appearances to the contrary.'

'You astound me!' Clementina exclaimed frankly. 'I must have supposed it to be an impossible task.'

Both the other ladies laughed out, but Clementina reddened a little, stammering, 'B-but I-I do not mean to be rude, ma'am.'

'Oh, stuff! In any event, on this occasion I am quite undone, for what do you suppose has happened? My son needs must insist on making an appearance. He is newly down from Oxford, you know, and has sworn to land me with a number of his cronies. Young graduates like himself. Lord knows what scaff-and-raff he will thrust upon me!'

'Heavens, yes!' agreed the dowager, amused. 'They let *anyone* into the universities in these days. You will likely find yourself playing hostess to a parcel of cits, Hetty.'

'Not quite as bad as that, I trust,' smiled her friend. 'But I will probably offend the sensibilities of some of our high-nosed dames.'

'Undoubtedly, ma'am,' Clementina said, twinkling, 'if my experiences are anything to go by.'

'You warned me, Alicia,' Lady Waldemar said delightedly, 'but I did not believe it! Well, there, Clementina—if I may call you so?—your re-

freshing candour is just what is needed here tomorrow night if these young gentlemen are to be
adequately entertained. I would I had a dozen like
you!'

'Dear me, I have not been so diverted for weeks!'
exclaimed Lady Staplegrove in an undervoice to her
young charge. 'We have stirred up my acquaintance to some purpose. As a result of our meander-
ings yesterday they are now consumed with curiosity
about you, do you see?'

'I thought they were all being very polite, ma'am,'
Clementina replied, looking a little puzzled.

'Oh, indeed. But it would surprise you to learn
how many of those who have come up to greet me
would in normal circumstances have merely bowed
and passed on. There is little amusement to be
gained from an old woman, you know. But when
she is known to be sponsoring a pretty young unknown girl the situation changes, as you see.'

She broke off to exchange greetings with another
of Lady Waldemar's guests, and to introduce Miss
Clementina Hythe.

'But I don't understand, ma'am,' Clementina
protested when they were once more alone. 'I
thought the purpose was to still tongues. Besides,
I would have thought that one more female among
all the débutantes must excite very little interest.'

The dowager gave a mischievous wink. 'Ah, but
I am Sothern's grandmother, don't forget. And,
naturally, everyone must suppose that your visit to
me means something.'

Clementina jumped. 'You mean they are imagining that he—that I—that we——?'

'His prospective bride, my child, would naturally claim my patronage,' laughed her ladyship. 'Is it not amusing?'

'No, it is not,' Clementina almost snapped. 'It is quite absurd. Moreover, I had thought you would dislike anything of that nature excessively.'

Lady Staplegrove regarded her in some amusement. 'Not in the least. I am only waiting until Sothern realises what is afoot, and my satisfaction will be complete.'

Clementina was silent. She could not believe that Jake would care tuppence for such idle speculation, but it came as something of a shock to hear Lady Staplegrove express herself in such terms, as if she would delight in her grandson's discomfiture.

If it were not for the circumstance of the interest she was exciting she would have enjoyed herself immensely, Clementina thought. For all her cynical views, the fashionable world held a certain fascination for a provincial, peopled as it was by those of the highest ton and exclusiveness. It was a circle she had never expected to enter, although her own background was nothing to be ashamed of. Lady Waldemar's rout was not a very large affair, but it was quite large enough to impress one used only to country assemblies.

Several of the downstairs rooms had been thrown open, but the décor was much more simple than that of the stifling blue saloon upstairs. It was in the design that their quality lay. The walls had been left white but for several arched panels which in the

Italian style had murals painted on them in chiaroscuro. The sepia tint was echoed on the mouldings of the ceilings and window arches, and the skirtings of the walls, and in the simple straw cushions and the cane of the few upright chairs.

Waiters moved among the throng with trays of dainties to eat and glasses of champagne, although there was more substantial fare to be had in the supper room at eleven o'clock. A room apart had been set aside for those who preferred to play at cards, but the vast majority of the company had congregated in these airy saloons, ambling about and engaging in conversation to the accompaniment of the muted strains of Mozart and Handel from a quartet of excellent musicians playing in a gallery above the hall.

Elegance characterised the guests. All was restrained, nothing showy. Jewels and buckles were few and dainty. A simple pendant miniature on a gold chain, a necklet of pearls, a bracelet of rhinestones and a pair of diamond earrings, or a jewelled comb or pin for the hair.

The gentlemen, scorning gems but for a pin in a cravat, were concerned more with the exquisite cut of their plain cloth or satin garments, the snowy whiteness of their intricately tied cravats, their short but deliberately careless hairstyles the only touch of disorder. Although a few of the older men adhered to their wigs, as they did to their rouged cheeks, and had their suits made slightly less close-fitting for comfort. The ladies wore pastel muslins and delicately figured silks that clung to their willowy forms, for thinness was the order of the

day. It was a fashion which did not deal kindly with
everyone, however. Unlike Lady Staplegrove and
her like, who kept sensibly to the waistline nature
had bestowed and stuck to the fashions of a few
years before, there were a number of foolish
matrons who attempted to confine their bosoms in
a tiny bodice, and unhappily draped their over-large
limbs in a mode which showed them to little advantage. Clementina was obliged to admit that they
looked ridiculous.

She derived considerable amusement from
watching the activities of the guests, her keen mind
enabling her very quickly to discern a variety of
relationships. The young débutante, unlike those
she had seen on yesterday's visit, who gushed avidly
over several different gentlemen, whom Clementina
took to be the eligibles present. The old man gazing
fatuously at an attractive lady who had eyes only
for her spouse, and who kept a jealous watch on
every other woman he spoke to. The two tabbies,
seated in a corner on a pair of straw-covered upright chairs, tattling together as they darted glances
from this person to that and whispered behind their
fans. Clementina's cheeks burned a little at the
thought of the prattling about her that must be
going on in just such a fashion. She was glad that
Jake was late.

When Lord Sothern finally arrived he was accompanied by the two friends who had been with
him the night Clementina had encountered them.
She recognised Sir Harry Blaine's florid countenance at once, but the other gentleman she had
taken less notice of, and it took a moment or two

for his features to reassert themselves on her
memory.

Jake did not approach them at once, and
Clementina lost sight of him for some time while
she was being held in conversation by one of the
matrons she had met yesterday, and who asked all
sorts of embarrassing questions. Clementina parried
them by pretending to shyness and referring them
to the dowager. Lady Staplegrove did not fail her,
turning off the flow with some queries of her own
on the matron's personal affairs.

When next Clementina noticed Lord Sothern he
was in close—and what looked like intimate—conversation with an opulent brunette whose ample
charms were imperfectly concealed by a diaphanous
gown cut low across the bosom. Clementina, who
was herself very prettily arrayed in the green muslin
half-dress which was the dowager's first choice for
her, thought with a little unexpected prick of envy
that the prevailing mode set off the woman's lovely
figure to admiration. What man could fail to admire
her?

'Lord above, I might have guessed she would be
here!' said Lady Staplegrove's voice behind her.

Clementina turned. 'Do you mean the lady
talking to Lord Sothern? Who is she, ma'am? She
is very beautiful.'

'Oh yes, extremely,' responded the dowager
acidly. 'Beautiful and lethal. She is Lady Matilda
Ingleby, and a disgrace to her sex. I had hoped
Sothern would have had more sense than to—but
that is neither here nor there.'

To her surprise, something inside Clementina seemed to go hollow all at once. That Jake and this Lady Matilda were lovers could not be in doubt. No other construction could be placed on the dowager's words.

She remembered suddenly the moment of tension between the two on the morning of her disastrous drive with the Earl. And he had said he had an engagement. Doubtless with his mistress. Then that is what people had supposed! That she had perhaps supplanted this woman in Sothern's arms. Again memory stirred. He had not visited his mistress that night. He had gone to Maria Spencer's musical soirée expressly to seek out Clementina herself. Not finding her, he had dashed to Brook Street and walked in on her when she was in that altogether compromising dishabille.

Clementina's cheeks flew colour as she recalled the look in Jake's face, the warmth of his hot gaze. Her eyes still on Lady Matilda Ingleby, she was seized by a sense of vague apprehension, the feminine instinct for danger. This woman was trouble.

'Why is she tolerated?' she enquired of the dowager, unconsciously betraying her understanding of the situation.

'She is the daughter of a Marquis,' said Lady Staplegrove drily. 'It is my belief that she only married Ingleby as a cover for her numerous *affaires*. He is much older than she. Not that it is any concern of mine how she conducts herself. If only she had not encouraged Jake to make a fool of himself over her.'

Clementina briefly pressed her hand. 'I am sorry, ma'am. It must be a severe trial for you to be obliged to be civil to her under the circumstances.'

'That, thank the Lord, I am spared!' uttered the dowager. 'She would not dare to approach me.'

An inadvertent chuckle escaped Clementina. 'I must admit I would give much to witness such an encounter.'

Lady Staplegrove burst out laughing. 'Clementina, you are a refreshing child. And worth a dozen of that . . .'

She paused a moment, looking again at Sothern's mistress. 'Do you know, I have just realised that she must have heard all the gossip and speculation concerning you. Ha!' she snorted gleefully. 'I hope very much that it may stick in her craw and choke her! What a famous joke if you were to cut her out! I declare, I could almost wish——'

She broke off abruptly, and Clementina saw that Jake was coming towards them. 'Good evening, Sothern. You have taken your time getting to us, I see. Doubtless you have many other more important acquaintance to greet first.'

The Earl bowed, unsmiling. 'Your pardon, ma'am.'

'There is no need to turn surly, Sothern,' the dowager said testily. 'For goodness' sake, pay some attention to the poor child! She is supposed to be your responsibility.'

With which, Lady Staplegrove left them together, and crossed the room to converse with her hostess. Sothern turned to Clementina.

'What has put her all on end, do you know?'

Clementina bit her lip, eyeing him. 'I'm not sure I ought to tell you.'

Jake's eyebrow went up, and he smiled faintly. 'You are not usually so reticent.'

Clementina shrugged. 'Well, it is not my affair, you know. Why don't you ask her yourself?'

'What? And give my head for washing? No, I thank you.'

'I imagine you can hold your own.'

'Not against Grandmama.'

Clementina chuckled. 'No, very true. I doubt if anyone could.'

Jake smiled, fully this time. 'Except perhaps yourself.'

She gave him one of her wide stares. 'What in the world makes you say that?'

'You are pretty outspoken already, you know. Or don't you know? And only eighteen as yet. I dread to imagine what you will be like in a few years' time.'

She chuckled again. 'Oh, don't say so! One of those dreadful, formidable matrons who terrify every man in sight.'

'Ah, that proves it!' exclaimed the Earl. 'You do not include women in the cowardly band, which shows how fearless you are, as you imagine all women to be.'

Clementina looked away. 'I fear some things.'

'Like the thing that made you run away, for instance?'

She glanced at him. 'You don't really expect me to fall into that trap, do you?'

Jake shook his head. 'Strange to say, it was not a trap. I was interested, that is all. But come,' he added, abruptly changing the subject. 'I want to re-acquaint you with a couple of friends of mine.'

He led her to where the Honourable Theodore Farleigh and Sir Harry Blaine were standing. Both were dressed in the mode, far neater than on the last occasion she had seen them. Although Sir Harry's rather stout figure did not appear to advantage in the extravagant satin knee-breeches and the flowered waistcoat he favoured, Farleigh looked very well in a quieter garb.

'Harry. Theo. I want to make you known to *my grandmother's* young friend, Miss Clementina Hythe,' he said, laying a warning stress on the words.

Sir Harry started and blinked at her. But Mr Farleigh stepped forward, and took her hand.

'Miss Hythe, a pleasure. What a fortunate thing that Lady Staplegrove invited you on a visit!'

'Is it not?' Clementina returned, a twinkle creeping into her eye. She looked enquiringly at Sir Harry, and a flush suffused his cheeks.

'Ma'am,' he managed, bowing slightly. 'I—er—I believe—that is, I hope——'

'You hope I will forgive you for reporting me to the constables?' Clementina enquired tranquilly.

'Clementina!' growled Jake as Sir Harry's cheeks became redder still and he glanced about to check if anyone was in earshot.

She threw Jake a mischievous glance. 'Yes, my lord? Did you expect me instead to thank him?'

'Don't try me too far, Miss Hythe,' he menaced in a low tone. 'I may be apt to forget I am a gentleman.'

'Yes, you have that tendency,' Clementina said in a considering tone, and turned back to his friends before he could respond. 'It is pleasant to meet you in these so much more comfortable circumstances. I hope that . . .'

Her voice died in mid-sentence and her eyes became fixed on some object behind the two gentlemen.

Jake frowned. 'Clementina?'

As he watched the colour drained slowly from her cheeks. He looked in the direction of her riveted gaze. Standing a few paces away, a young man— and one extraordinarily handsome—was staring at Clementina, a look on his face of the blankest astonishment.

Jake glanced back at her. Her face was paper-white and there was shock in her eyes. And fear.

CHAPTER FIVE

LORD SOTHERN took Clementina's arm and shook it. 'Clementina! What is it? Who is that man?'

She stood as if rooted to the spot, and did not seem to hear him. Jake glanced back at the man, but he had disappeared into the throng of people. He looked at the two puzzled faces of his friends.

'Did you see him? Do either of you know him?'

'I beg your pardon, old fellow, but I didn't really notice,' Theo told him apologetically.

'Harry?'

'Saw the fellow, all right,' Sir Harry said, 'but can't say I recognised him. Dare say he's one of these devilish Oxford fellows young Waldemar has in tow. Rank outsiders, most of 'em! Shouldn't be allowed.'

Sothern turned back to Clementina, whose arm he had been firmly holding all the while. Anxious to avoid attracting unnecessary attention, he tweaked her fingers sharply. She shivered, blinked and looked up at him, her eyes blank for a moment.

'Come and sit down,' Jake ordered curtly.

Clementina came to, and the hubbub of the party was suddenly loud in her ears. She felt sick and dizzy. But there was Jake, trying to drag her off. She pulled herself together.

'No, I am all right,' she said in a shaky voice. 'If I might just have a glass of water.'

'I'll get it,' Theo offered, and disappeared into the crowd.

Jake led her to a caned chair, and obliged her to sit down. 'I don't want you falling down in a faint.' He took her fan from her, and began to wave it to and fro before her face.

Clementina took a few steadying breaths. Becoming aware of her surroundings again, she became conscious of someone's eyes upon her. She was looking straight into the face of Sothern's mistress. What she saw there made her speak without thinking.

'Oh, Jake, do stop that! Or give my fan to Sir Harry. Lady Matilda is looking quite daggers at me!'

The fan shut with a snap, and she saw Lord Sothern stiffen alarmingly. On her other side Sir Harry gave a gasp. Realising what she had said, she flushed scarlet.

'Oh, dear! I—I did not mean——' she stammered. 'That is—it—it slipped out. I beg your pardon, my lord!'

'It is of no consequence,' Sothern said abruptly. He passed the fan to his friend. 'Harry, perhaps you will assist Miss Hythe.'

As he walked away Clementina gazed after him in some dismay. She turned to Sir Harry.

'I have seriously offended him, have I not?'

Sir Harry coughed. 'Very sensitive, do you see, where Maud's concerned.'

'Maud?'

'Lady Matilda, I should say. Doesn't mind it when he shocks the world, do you see? But can't bear to be laughed at.'

'Do they laugh at him?' Clementina asked, feeling quite irrationally annoyed with the fashionable world.

Sir Harry coughed again. 'Not his conquest, do you see? But her triumph. Stings his pride.'

Clementina nodded. 'Yes, I see.'

'And—er—what with all the hoo-ha over——' He broke off, reddening, and coughed. 'Forget what I was going to say.'

She looked him straight in the eye. 'Over me. That is what you meant, is it not?'

He was spared having to answer this by the arrival of Mr Farleigh at this moment with her glass of water. She sipped it thoughtfully, her eyes following Lady Matilda's progress around the room. Of Lord Sothern there was no sign.

But neither of that pair occupied her thoughts for long. These rapidly became fully taken up with the immediate problem confronting her. Where had he disappeared to now, the young man whose appearance had so startled her? What he was doing in London she could not imagine. She had not thought he had the entrée to such affairs as these. From somewhere in a nebulous cloud of memory Sir Harry's words about young Lord Waldemar floated back to her. His Oxford friends! And had not Lady Waldemar herself spoken of them yesterday? No doubt that was precisely how that devil had gained entrance here. She could not imagine that he had befriended the young Viscount for any other purpose, in fact. Typical it was of him that he should so use people.

Clementina sighed a little. She was undone for certain! What was she to do now? She must think quickly, and take action. She looked at Theo.

'Did you see Lady Staplegrove when you were absent, Mr Farleigh?'

'Oh yes, ma'am. She is in the card-room.'

'Is she playing?'

'I believe not. Would you wish me to fetch her?'

'Not for the world. If—if you would not mind keeping me company, I shall just wait for her to come. I would not wish to destroy her enjoyment of the party.'

It was not very many minutes later, however, that Lady Staplegrove came looking for her. She was displeased to find that Lord Sothern had abandoned her, but glad that Clementina was ready to return home. She talked at length in the carriage of the various entertainments in store, anticipating with some enjoyment the reactions of her numerous acquaintance to the comedy she felt she had set up for them. She did not notice that Clementina was strangely silent.

Nor did she think it odd when her protegée did not appear at the breakfast table next morning. But at eleven o'clock she popped up to let Clementina know that she was going out to visit the gross Lady Seagrave again, and was surprised to find the bed made up and no sign of her charge.

As Lady Staplegrove walked into the room a sense of foreboding gripped her. She glanced about and at once saw the folded sheet of notepaper propped up against the dressing-table mirror. It was addressed to herself. She snatched it up, and swiftly mastered the contents. They told her nothing more than that Clementina thanked her from the heart for all her kindness, and was sorry to be obliged to leave without bidding her a proper farewell and thanking her in person. No word of explanation for her flight was offered.

For a few moments the dowager could not think at all beyond the fact that Clementina had gone. To her own surprise she felt tears pricking her eyes.

'Have I become so fond of the child in so short a time?' she asked herself aloud. 'What in the world should I do now?'

She walked slowly from the room and down the stairs to the pink parlour where she usually sat when she had no company.

It was her favourite retreat, for besides being of a comfortable size its plain white walls and the pleasant pink of its furnishings gave it a cosy air. Moreover, as it was situated beside the front door, it offered an extremely convenient position for her ladyship to spy upon her callers. She could peep through the lace under-curtain without being seen, and decide whether or not she wished to be at home to the visitors. Then she might dart to the door and inform her understanding butler by a series of grimaces and jerky motions of her hands whether or not to admit the caller. Dorridge would then conduct the favoured to the green saloon, where the dowager would presently join them.

Sothern, of course, being well versed in his grandmother's habits, was apt to barge straight into her sanctum. But in fact the butler knew that her grandson was one of the few persons ever admitted to the pink parlour. He had naturally added the privileged Miss Clementina Hythe to the list, although, in the light of recent events, he might be forgiven for beginning to wonder whether her ladyship's hitherto undisputed title to the comforts of the pink parlour was not about to be challenged.

Lady Staplegrove, however, in her natural agitation, merely gravitated to the place out of a need for concentrated thought.

On impulse, she rang the bell and then sat down at her writing desk to compose a note for her grandson.

'Ah, Dorridge,' she said as soon as the butler entered. 'Do you have any idea when Miss Clementina left the house this morning?'

The butler shook his head. 'None, your ladyship. Shall I enquire among the servants?'

'Yes, do so. And send me a footman to take a note to Lord Sothern at once. And another to go to Mount Street. I cannot after all visit Lady Seagrave this morning.'

Jake arrived in record time, having driven himself from Brooks, where the dowager had had the forethought to send the footman. She jumped up from her chair and went quickly towards him, her hands held out.

'Thank heaven you are come, Sothern! I am quite distracted with worry.'

The Earl took her hands and held them tightly. 'I have sent for Cullen to join me here. Together we must be able to locate her.'

'Do you think so, indeed? I cannot for the life of me understand what should make her run away like this.' Lady Staplegrove looked searchingly into her grandson's face. 'You know something,' she remarked shrewdly.

Jake released her hands and turned away. 'I blame myself. Something occurred to distress her, and instead of pursuing it I—well, I took offence at some remark she made and left her.'

'Lady Maud!' said the dowager instantly. 'I might have known.'

Sothern's head snapped round. He was frowning. 'So it was you who let the cat out of the bag! May I ask, ma'am, what my affairs have to do with a chit of Clementina's age? Or why you should be so lost to all sense of decorum as to discuss them with her?'

Lady Staplegrove drew herself up. 'If you, sir, had enough sense of decency to refrain from making a spectacle of your affairs in public it would not fall to me to gloss over what must be obvious to the meanest intelligence!'

Flushing darkly, her grandson glared at her. 'Accept my apologies for causing you any embarrassment, ma'am,' he said stiffly.

'Oh, for the Lord's sake, come down off your high ropes,' the dowager begged tartly, 'and tell me at once what occurred to distress the child.'

Some of the anger left Jake's brow. 'It had nothing whatsoever to do with Maud.'

'Yes, yes, very well. Get on, do.'

'She saw someone she knew,' Sothern said curtly. 'A young man. He recognised her, too, that was clear enough. She was almost ready to swoon, the shock was so severe. I made her sit down, and Theo went to get her some water. But she would not tell me who he was. Then——' He broke off and went to stand by the window so that he might watch his groom walking his horses instead of having to encounter his grandmother's keen glance.

'Then?' Lady Staplegrove prompted.

'She noticed Maud watching us, and referred to it. That is all. I took offence, even though she apologised instantly.' He paused, drew a breath, and resumed. 'I—I really don't know why I reacted that way. I could not more sufficiently regret it, for this is the outcome.'

'Oh, fiddle!' scoffed the dowager. 'You do not mean to imply that she left us for such a petty cause as that? Clementina has more sense.'

He looked round. 'Not that, no. But if I had probed more I might have learned something. Or at least have led her to feel that she could rely on my protection rather than have gone out into the world alone again.'

His grandmother was silent. Seeing him writhing under unaccustomed remorse twisted her heartstrings. For all his faults, and the times his conduct exasperated her, she loved him dearly. She might have wished such feelings on him, but to see it was another matter. She turned the subject.

'Can you think of any way you may discover where she has gone?'

Jake sighed. 'No. But I am hoping our man of business may assist me. He can make enquiries about this Major Henlow, for instance, and perhaps discover in what way Clementina is concerned with him. Did none of the servants see her leave?'

Lady Staplegrove shook her head. 'No, but one of the maids is missing. I am hopeful she may have accompanied the child.'

Jake's brow lightened. 'That would be a relief, certainly.'

At this moment Dorridge entered the room. Both the dowager and Lord Sothern turned eagerly.

'Mr Cullen has arrived, my lady. I have put him in the bookroom.'

A practice which was the butler's invariable habit with callers other than those of the highest *ton*. It did not find favour with his mistress on this occasion, however.

'The bookroom? What in the world for? Send him in here, man, send him in here,' said Lady Staplegrove impatiently.

Dorridge coughed. 'There is one other matter, my lady.'

'Well, go on.'

'The maid, Lucy, has returned. She denies having seen Miss Clementina, my lady, but it is my belief she is lying. Would you wish to question her yourself?'

'I had better see her,' said her ladyship decidedly. 'And you may tell her that she may well find herself turned off without a character if I find she is lying to me.'

Jake intervened. 'Wait, Dorridge. Grandmama, you will not get the truth out of the girl by such means. Say nothing, Dorridge. Just send the girl in.'

As the door closed behind the butler Lady Staplegrove raised her brows at her grandson. 'I suppose you mean to worm the truth out of the girl with that famous charm of yours.'

Jake grinned. 'I'll wager I get more by it than you would with the threat of dismissal.'

Lady Staplegrove snorted. But before she could pursue the matter there was a knock at the door, and Mr Cullen was announced.

He was a spare man in his mid-fifties, clad in sober garments and the old-fashioned wig typical of his calling, and he was invariably seen with a pair of pince-nez perched on his nose. He greeted his clients punctiliously, and apologised for being late.

'I was obliged to conclude a matter of business before leaving the office, my lord. I hope I have not inconvenienced you.'

Lord Sothern disclaimed, and invited him to sit down. He politely waited until the dowager had seated herself on the pink brocade sofa, and took a chair opposite.

'What may I have the honour of doing for your ladyship?'

'I doubt if you can do anything,' frankly responded the dowager. 'But Sothern seems to feel you can help us. We've lost a girl.'

Mr Cullen gazed at her blankly. 'Lost a girl, my lady?'

Jake smiled, and came forward to sit beside his grandmother. 'Allow me, ma'am. This is a matter of some delicacy, Cullen.'

The lawyer extracted his spectacles from an inner pocket, and through them surveyed the Earl. 'I am all attention, my lord.'

'Three nights ago, Cullen, I accidentally came upon a young lady in need of help and protection. She was masquerading as a boy and had obviously run away, but would tell me nothing of her circumstances. I brought her to stay with Lady Staplegrove, and she attended a party with us last night. This morning, however, she has run away again. I want your help to find her. The matter is to be treated, I need scarcely say, with the greatest confidentiality.'

'You may rely on me, my lord, as I hope you know,' Cullen said, apparently unmoved by the oddity of the story. He cleared his throat. 'Did you glean any information at all about the young lady, my lord? Her name, perhaps? Or did she use an alias?'

'No. She was going to, but the truth slipped out. She is a Miss Clementina Hythe.'

The lawyer's spectacles shifted comically as his jaw dropped. 'Miss Hythe? But I have just seen her! She came to my office this very morning.'

The lawyer's startling announcement was productive of a sudden silence. It was broken by a discreet knock at the door.

'Come,' called Lady Staplegrove automatically, and turned to see the frightened face of a housemaid peeping round the parlour door.

The Earl was on his feet. 'Are you certain of this, Cullen? You have the name right?'

'Quite certain, my lord,' affirmed the lawyer, rising also. Noticing the girl who was entering in response to Lady Staplegrove's imperiously beckoning finger, he almost started. 'Why, this is the very maid who accompanied Miss Hythe, if I am not very much mistaken!'

'So!' pronounced her ladyship awfully. 'You saw fit to lie to Dorridge, Lucy. You have not seen Miss Clementina this morning, indeed!'

Lucy, gulping with fright, and staring at Mr Cullen with popping eyes, dropped a curtsy and twisted her apron in her fingers.

'I—I beg your pardon, ma'am. Miss said—Miss made me promise not to tell.'

'That is neither here nor there, my girl,' began her ladyship. 'You are——'

'Please, Grandmama!' Sothern interrupted. 'I can well imagine how Clementina worked upon the girl. You are yourself not immune to her charms, remember.'

Lady Staplegrove was momentarily silenced, and his lordship crossed to the maid and patted her shoulder reassuringly.

'Come, Lucy, there is no need to be afraid. You have only to tell the truth, and I will engage for it that her ladyship will not punish you. Just tell us what happened, if you please.'

No less susceptible than any other young female, the maid blushed at his lordship's touch, and dropped another curtsy.

'Well, sir, I had no notion of Miss leaving the house at first. I mean, when I went to make up the fire in her room early, like I do all the rooms, my lord. And there Miss was, all dressed up and wrapping her things up in a shawl, like.'

'In a *shawl*?' echoed Lady Staplegrove, her brows rising.

'Y-yes, ma'am,' Lucy faltered, her eyes flicking a scared glance in her mistress's direction. 'It—it didn't look seemly to me neither, ma'am.'

Sothern suppressed a smile. 'Go on,' he said encouragingly.

'Well, sir, Miss looked at me, a bit surprised, like, I thought. She said she didn't think as how the servants were up yet. "Lordy, miss!" says I, "the likes of us don't lie abed till all hours. We——"'

'Yes, yes. Get on with it, girl,' interpolated Lady Staplegrove impatiently.

'Yes, ma'am. Sorry, ma'am,' said Lucy, subsiding. 'Then—then Miss asked me could I keep a secret, and—and she said she had to go away quiet like because—because...' The girl glanced up at the Earl with a look mingled of respect and censure. Then out it came in a rush. 'Because your lordship meant to give her up to them as is a-persecuting of her.'

Lord Sothern's eyes flicked heavenwards. 'I might have known I would be cast as the villain of the piece!'

His grandmother snorted. 'Your just deserts, Sothern. Even if not strictly accurate.'

Jake ignored her. 'Please continue, Lucy.'

'There's—there's not much to tell, sir,' said the puzzled maid. 'I got Miss a cloak-bag for her things, and went with her to this gentleman's place in the

City for to fetch her some money. Miss said as how she would hire a coach. And we goes to the Register Office to get her an abigail to travel with her. That's where I left her, sir. She puts me in a cab and give me the fare, and warns me as how to say nothing to nobody. And—and that's all I know, sir.'

'Thank you, Lucy. You have been very helpful,' Jake told her with his charming smile. 'And don't worry your head over betraying a secret. You have done Miss Clementina a far greater service by doing so than you would have done by keeping it.'

Gratified, the maid curtsied and thanked him, and, at a sign from Lady Staplegrove, left the room. Her mistress then looked at the lawyer.

'Well, Cullen? How much of this story can you corroborate?'

The lawyer settled his spectacles. 'I cannot vouch for the accuracy of all the girl's story, my lady,' he began scrupulously, 'but Miss Hythe did indeed come to me for money, explaining that she had an urgent need to go to her old home in Dunhythe. I offered to send one of my lads to hire the coach for her, but she informed me—mendaciously it now appears——' he added, with a frown of disapproval, 'that this was already being arranged by Major Henlow's footman, who accompanied her.' The frown deepened. 'She also gave me to understand that the young female was her own abigail, and that she had but that moment arrived in town from Rye. Which, if I understand you correctly, my lord, was a complete fabrication.'

'Entirely,' drawled the Earl. 'An enterprising young lady, Miss Clementina Hythe. Too enterprising for her own good.'

'Oh, fiddle, Sothern! She has been remarkably clever,' remarked Lady Staplegrove. 'At least we now know where she has gone. And it is a relief to find that she had the sense not to travel by coach alone.'

'*If* she indeed hired a maid,' Jake pointed out.

His grandmother started. 'Oh, no. You don't feel that she fibbed about that, too?'

'I should think it extremely probable. Lucy did not, after all, actually see her enter the Register Office. We have only Clementina's doubtful word for it that she was actually going to hire a coach. Or even that Dunhythe is her intended destination. In fact, Grandmama, we cannot be sure of anything at all.'

'Do you mean you will not go after her, then?' demanded the dowager in some severity.

'Of course I shall go after her. But not before I have heard everything Cullen can tell us about her.' He looked at the lawyer. 'Who is she, Cullen? And just exactly how does she stand in relationship to this Major Henlow?'

'Dear me!' exclaimed the dowager. 'How did I come to forget that? Tell us everything, Cullen. At once!'

The lawyer inclined his head and coughed delicately. 'You will, I am assured, treat all I say with the utmost confidence. Miss Hythe is in some sort my client, and——'

'Yes, yes, to be sure,' impatiently agreed Lady Staplegrove. 'Do get on, man.'

'Very well, my lady.' He reseated himself, and addressed his opening remarks to the dowager. 'I was man of business to Miss Hythe's late father, Sir Clement Hythe. Dunhythe is the family property, situated in Norfolk.'

A frown creased Jake's brow. 'Yes, that much I had ascertained. But surely the property has passed on? What would it avail Clementina to go there? Unless she has other relatives in possession, perhaps?'

'Not at all, my lord. The estate is most foolishly left.' He coughed. 'Sir Clement had something of a bee in his bonnet on certain matters, and this is the outcome.'

'You speak in riddles, Cullen,' interrupted Lady Staplegrove. 'Do make sense, man, for the Lord's sake!'

'I beg your pardon, ma'am.'

'Give him a chance, Grandmama,' Jake admonished. He ignored her glare, and bent his most charming smile on his man of business. 'Do go on, Cullen. But strive to be brief. I must go after Clementina as soon as may be.'

'I will endeavour, my lord. The house and grounds, being under entail, have passed to the heir. With the title, of course. But unfortunately they are of little use to the lad, my lord, for the rest of the estate, and *all* the money, is left in trust to Miss Hythe.'

'He cut up the estate?' uttered Lady Staplegrove in disbelieving tones. 'He must have been mad!'

'Not mad, my lady. Merely prudent.' Again the lawyer gave a delicate cough. 'And perhaps, shall we say, a trifle vengeful. You see, Sir Jeremy Hythe, as he is now known, is most unfortunately a simpleton.'

'A half-wit? Or crazy?' asked the Earl.

'Backward, my lord.'

'Oh, poor boy!' said the dowager, her ready sympathy stirred. 'But he is cared for? His parents, perhaps, or——?'

'His father died many years ago. He was Sir Clement's younger brother. His mother remarried, and——'

'Major Henlow?' guessed the Earl.

'Correct, my lord.'

'But, gracious heaven, what a monster!' ejaculated Lady Staplegrove. 'Is this all Sir Clement's reason for cutting the poor boy out? Because he is a simpleton?'

'I think it is rather Major Henlow whom Sir Clement desired to keep out, my lady. He—er—traded on the relationship in such a manner that I believe Sir Clement became suspicious of his motives. Major Henlow has, or had in the past, a tendency to live rather expensively, probably well beyond his means. Sir Clement had it fixed in his head that the gentleman was bent upon enriching himself at young Mr Jeremy's expense.'

'Then what in Hades possessed him to leave Clementina to the guardianship of such a man?' exploded Lord Sothern wrathfully.

'He did not do so, my lord. In fact, he did not name a guardian at all. Nothing could have been

further from his own mind than an early demise,'
Cullen explained. 'It is young Sir Jeremy who has
become her guardian, by virtue of the fact that he
is her nearest male relative living.'

'Absurd!' scoffed Lady Staplegrove.

'Why, so I think, my lady. But such is indeed the
case. Mrs Henlow naturally invited her niece to live
with them in Rye, at least until such time as the
tangle might be sorted out.'

Silence fell. The dowager, too shocked to speak,
was staring at Cullen as if she could not believe her
ears. Her grandson, looking thoughtful, paced a
step or two about the room. Then he looked at the
lawyer.

'Well, one thing is evident. Whatever means they
had hit upon to untangle this coil, it was not to
Clementina's taste! Tell me, has this Henlow any
children of his own?'

'A son, my lord.'

'Ah! What age?'

'Oh, he must be nineteen or twenty by now, my
lord.'

'Must he indeed?' said Jake softly. 'And not a
half-wit, I trust? Not congenitally deformed?'

'By no means. I believe Mr Ellis Henlow to be
an extremely personable young man.'

CHAPTER SIX

LADY STAPLEGROVE'S eyebrows rose in a look of exaggerated surprise as she stared at her visitors.

'I confess I am at a loss, sir. Your niece, you say?'

The elder of the two gentlemen smiled unctuously. 'My most treasured niece. Alas, ma'am! I have not known a moment's peace since she left the protection of her home.'

The faint, sympathetic smile which the dowager bestowed upon him gave no clue to her thoughts. They were not much in the gentleman's favour. Even had she had no reason to despise Major Henlow, Lady Staplegrove felt she could not have liked him. Not that he was ill-favoured. On the contrary, the years, which she judged to be some fifty odd, had treated him kindly. Some greying at the temples and a slight portliness of figure were offset by a pleasant countenance and an air of good-humoured benevolence. He was neatly dressed, though frock-coated in a countrified way.

It was rather his manner that had caused her ladyship impulsively to deny all knowledge of Clementina. A studied obsequiousness, together with a calculating look in the eye, gave her an instant mistrust of him when he greeted her upon her entrance into the green saloon with an effusive expression of gratitude for her care of his runaway niece.

'I am naturally sorry for your distress, sir,' she responded, 'but I fail to see what this has to do with me.'

'Ah, ma'am!' sighed the Major. 'I understand you, I believe. You seek to protect Clementina. You believe, perhaps, that I am not who I purport to be. Only bring her to me and you will have all the proofs you require on her own recognition of her loving uncle.'

With difficulty, Lady Staplegrove refrained from bursting into intemperate speech. A *loving* uncle, indeed! When she knew him to be anything but.

'You mistake, sir,' she said instead, with the utmost sweetness. 'Believe me, you mistake. I have no knowledge of this—Clementina, did you say?'

'I beg your ladyship's pardon,' bowed Major Henlow, 'but it will not do. You see, my son was at Lady Waldemar's rout last evening.'

Her ladyship's brows rose in hauteur. 'I trust he was well entertained.'

'As to that, ma'am, I cannot say. But he will tell you himself what he saw.' He beckoned to the fair young man who had been standing in the background quietly observing the scene. 'Allow me to present my son, Lady Staplegrove. Ellis, make your bow.'

Mr Henlow stepped forward into the light that streamed in from the window, and Lady Staplegrove suffered a momentary surprise. What a handsome creature! The thought escaped her involuntarily.

Clementina must be blind not to have fallen madly in love with him.

But as he rose from an elegant bow he gave her a smile which twisted his mouth almost into a sneer, a smile as calculated as his father's eyes, and which did not even reach his own. The dowager found no difficulty in disliking him intensely on the instant.

'My lady,' he began, in a voice silky-smooth and cold, 'I saw my cousin last night, in company with your grandson. So shocked was I that I believed at first I must have been mistaken. A few pertinent enquiries, however, elicited the interesting intelligence that the girl was indeed Miss Clementina Hythe, and that she is a guest in your home.'

The grey eyes looked down into Lady Staplegrove's face with cool insolence, evidently in expectation of a blustering reply. But the dowager was made of sterner stuff than that. She had taken pains to inform the world of Clementina's visit, had introduced her candidly as Miss Hythe. But she would deny it in the teeth of them all, should any dare to espouse the Henlows' cause! What could they do in the face of such denial? Nothing at all. Let them but try, that was all. Let them but try!

Giving him back look for look, she raised her brows disdainfully. 'Then, sir, I have only to say that you were misinformed.'

Major Henlow pushed forward. 'Maybe so, ma'am. Maybe so. But at least you will not deny that Miss Hythe was at the rout?'

'My dear sir,' haughtily responded her ladyship, 'as I am wholly unacquainted with Miss Hythe, I am afraid I cannot say.'

Young Mr Henlow smiled unpleasantly. 'I wonder if Lord Sothern will be similarly unable to say.'

'My grandson is out of town.'

Ellis Henlow gave a short laugh. 'I'll warrant he is.'

'Ellis, that will do!' Major Henlow again turned on his false smile. 'Lady Staplegrove, I do beg of you to reconsider. I am perfectly aware that you are trying only to help my niece, but I promise you this attitude you have adopted is quite mistaken.'

The dowager drew herself up, only too ready for battle. 'Do you dare to threaten me, Major Henlow?'

'Oh no, no, no! Upon my honour, you take me up quite wrongly. I meant only to convey that I intend no harm to the child. She will be quite safe with us. Her flight was due to a sorry misunderstanding. Indeed, I heartily regret that I did not clear the matter up more thoroughly. Nothing was further from my mind than to drive her to run away.'

Lady Staplegrove snorted. 'These protestations had better have been addressed to your niece, sir.'

'And would be,' riposted the Major instantly, 'were you but to allow me to see her, if only for a few moments.'

'I have told you, Major Henlow, that I know nothing of the girl.'

'Then how comes it about, ma'am,' Ellis Henlow interrupted, 'that the Earl of Sothern embroiled himself in the affairs of a runaway wanted by the Bow——?'

'Be silent,' snapped his father.

'Why? What does it matter? Her ladyship is clearly set on concealing my cousin. It is evident you will gain nothing by your expressions of——'

'Will you hold your tongue, sir?' thundered his parent. He turned to the dowager. 'I make you my apologies, ma'am. My son is too distressed by this business to know what he is saying. I assure you——'

'There is no need of your assurances, sir,' said Lady Staplegrove acidly. 'Since Mr Henlow so obviously believes me to be hiding your niece from you, perhaps you would care to search the house?'

'A waste of time,' snapped the younger man before his father could reply. 'It is clear that Clementina is no longer here. We may as well proceed to Dunhythe.' His mouth twisted sardonically. 'Since his lordship has left town in something of a hurry, perhaps he has chosen to escort her?'

The Major looked much struck by this suggestion. 'Good God, Ellis! I believe you may be right.' He glanced at Lady Staplegrove. 'Is it so, ma'am?'

The dowager hesitated just a shade too long before replying. 'I am not Sothern's keeper, sir. He—he is out of town. That is all.'

It was enough. Young Mr Henlow smiled in triumph. 'Thank you, ma'am. You have told me all I wish to know. We will wish you a very good day. Come, sir.'

He left the room on the words, and Major Henlow, pausing only to bid his reluctant hostess a hasty farewell, soon followed.

Lady Staplegrove waited until she heard the front door close, and then crossed to the fireplace to tug violently upon the bell-pull. While she waited for the summons to be answered she thought how readily she could believe in the history Cullen had told her. From the contrast between his father's bucolic appearance and Ellis Henlow's expensive, fashionable attire it was all too obvious where Clementina's money was going to go, should they get their hands on it.

Dorridge came in to find his mistress pacing up and down the green saloon in mingled anxiety and fury. It was as well it was sparsely furnished. For this was the apartment commonly in use on more formal occasions, and though there were sofas and chairs, covered in green satin, ranged around the walls, they were rather built for elegance than comfort. Gilt finishings to the mantelshelf, the mirrors and the candelabra, the massive chandelier, and various portraits ranged about the green-striped brocade of the walls—including the family group by Mr Gainsborough and that done by the then highly favoured Sir Joshua Reynolds of Lady Staplegrove herself in younger days—all added to the stuffy air of formality.

But at least there was plenty of room to accommodate her ladyship's agitated pacing. She pounced on the butler as he entered.

'Dorridge, at last! What an age you have been! You must send immediately for Cullen. No, wait!'

She paused, gnawing at a fingertip. 'Yes, I have it. Forget about Cullen. Send someone to find either Sir Harry Blaine or Mr Theodore Farleigh. One or the other. I don't care which. Or even both, if they should happen to be together.'

The butler gazed at her blankly. Her ladyship almost stamped her foot.

'Well, don't stand there staring, man! Get along, do.'

Dorridge bowed. He spoke stiffly. 'Having located these gentlemen, my lady, what would you wish the footman to say to them?'

'Say to them? Say to them? Lord above, Dorridge! Don't be a fool! Summon them here to me. On the instant, Dorridge. The matter is of the utmost urgency.'

Less than an hour later both Blaine and the Honourable Theodore Farleigh were to be seen riding in a northerly direction out of London, their horses at a canter, with orders to chase after Lord Sothern and warn him that the Henlows were hard on his heels.

It was doubtful whether they would catch up with him for some considerable time, for he had made good speed in his phaeton which was pulled by four fast horses, in spite of stopping several times to enquire about the occupants of any coaches that might be on the road ahead of him. While he placed little dependence on Clementina's having hired a coach at all, it was as well to check at the various posthouses on the way. There were, he learned, at least three ladies travelling in company with one other female that day, and although the postboy's vague descriptions placed two well above Clementina's age, there was no saying but his quarry might well have been the third.

Accordingly Sothern kept to the main stopping-places on the route, and would not have bothered to investigate a little-frequented wayside inn just beyond Ponders End had not one of his horses cast a shoe.

Cursing freely, Jake limped the phaeton into the yard of the Little Foxes, and demanded the where-abouts of a smithy. The landlord arranged to send the horse with one of his boys, and invited his lordship to partake of refreshment in the coffee-room.

'For yer honour won't care to sit in the tap, and there's nobbut a lad in the coffee-room to disturb yer honour.'

His lordship graciously consenting to share the coffee-room, he was ushered into a small apartment furnished with a couple of dressers and a large round table. At this, opposite the door, was seated a fair young man who looked up as the door opened.

He let out a gasp and jumped up, upsetting a large coffee-pot. And the Earl found himself gazing blankly into a piquant little face with a pair of startled green eyes.

'My God!' Sothern ejaculated.

'Jake,' uttered Clementina in a stupefied voice. 'What are you...? How——?'

She broke off, noticing the landlord's open-mouthed astonishment, and flushed uncomfortably. Seeing the spreading coffee-stain on the white tablecloth, she busied herself with a futile attempt at mopping it up with a napkin.

Lord Sothern pulled himself together, and turned to the goggling landlord. 'Well, this is a fortunate coincidence. I little thought to run into a friend in this out-of-the-way place. Some wine, landlord, if you please. This calls for a celebration.'

'But the cloth, yer honour...' the landlord protested.

'Yes, yes. You may see to it later. The damage is minimal. See? My friend has already attended to the worst of it. The wine, man! I'm devilish thirsty.'

With which, he thrust the landlord willy-nilly from the room, and shut the door upon him. Then he turned to confront Clementina. But before he could say anything at all she rushed into speech.

'How in the world did you find me? And what do you mean by chasing after me? I am perfectly well able to handle my affairs for myself, and I don't require your assistance!'

'Softly, my child, softly,' Jake chided. 'As it happens, I found you quite by chance. I have been diligently following the post-road and checking for you at the coaching inns.' A smile lurked in his eyes. 'I half suspected some trickery, however. Though I confess it had not occurred to me that you would revert to your male attire.'

'I couldn't very well ride dressed as a female, could I?' Clementina said defensively.

Jake frowned. 'You are not *riding*?'

'Why not?'

'All the way to Norfolk?'

'Why shouldn't I? I ride perfectly well.'

'I don't doubt it. But you will exhaust yourself.'

'No, I won't. I am taking easy stages. Besides, if anyone follows me, I should attract less attention.'

'As we see,' remarked Jake drily.

Clementina clenched her fists. 'Yes, you *would* come up with me, wouldn't you? Why can't you leave me alone?'

'Don't you think I feel some responsibility, having taken it upon myself to intervene in your affairs already?' asked Jake gently.

'My affairs have nothing to do with you,' Clementina snapped crossly. 'I wish you will go away and leave me to manage on my own.'

Jake was prevented from replying by the re-entrance of the landlord, bearing a tray with two glasses and a bottle of wine. He insisted on covering the damaged cloth with a fresh one, however, before Jake could get rid of him. Pouring the wine, his lordship held one glass out to Clementina.

'I don't want it,' she said ungraciously.

'Drink it and don't be childish,' Jake told her peremptorily.

Clementina glared at him. 'Do you imagine you can order me about in such a fashion?'

Jake grinned. 'Dear Clementina, do please—just to oblige me—have a little wine.'

Grudgingly she took the glass, and Sothern invited her to reseat herself. Then he took a chair near her, and sat at his ease, studying her face over the rim of his wine glass. Uncomfortable under this scrutiny, Clementina looked away from him.

'Well, what now?' she asked gruffly.

'Now, my indomitable young friend, you are going to tell me all about your step-uncle, Major Henlow, and your cousin, Sir Jeremy Hythe, and young Mr Henlow whom you saw at Lady Waldemar's, and whose appearance there led you to run away again.'

Clementina stared at him, the green eyes wide. 'How do you know about them? How *could* you know?'

Jake's smile was rueful. 'I'm afraid you miscalculated, my child. You see, Mr Cullen is also *my* man of business.'

'Oh.' Clementina's gaze did not waver, but a shade of reserve came into her face. 'Then you know—a great deal.'

Sothern shook his head. 'No, my dear. As you are perfectly well aware, Cullen knows nothing more than the tangle in which your father left your inheritance.'

'It was not his fault,' Clementina said quickly. 'How could Papa imagine that a slight chill would lead to his death?'

Jake placed a hand briefly over hers where it lay clenched on the table. 'I am laying no blame. Indeed, how could I, when I know nothing of the circumstances? But that you are in grave difficulties through this mismanagement I do know. I want to help you.' His mouth curved into that charming smile. 'You must confide in someone, Clementina. I know that you are *almost* nineteen, but that is not a very great age. Come, can you not do with some assistance?'

Clementina sighed. 'I don't see what you can do to help.'

'That we shall see. I can't tell until I know the circumstances, however.'

She looked at him. Then away again. 'They want me to marry Jeremy,' she said abruptly.

'What, the half-wit?' Jake ejaculated, shocked. 'You cannot be serious!'

Clementina lifted her glass and sipped the wine, calm now that the thing was said. 'He is not exactly a half-wit, you know. At least, he is simple, but not stupid. He can think very well for himself, but he is so slow, poor Jeremy.'

Jake controlled himself with an effort. He did not know what he had expected, but it was certainly not that. The idea of this quick-witted, courageous girl tied to a simpleton, and condemned to a life which he did not care to contemplate, was intolerable. It also appeared futile. What did the Henlows stand to gain from such an alliance?

'I don't see how such a marriage would serve them,' he said, his voice carefully neutral.

'No more did I,' confessed Clementina frankly. 'At first, that is.' She looked at Jake, and there was hurt in the green eyes. 'That is what upset me so much when I knew he had called in the Runners. You see, the Major pretended that it was all for our sakes—mine and Jeremy's. A way to sort out the mess without the least bother. For what is the title and the house to Jeremy without the revenue from the estates? I quite see that. As for me, what else was there? There could be no question of my coming out and finding a husband in the usual way.

I am well dowered, of course, for the estates are worth something, but there is little ready money to be had for the expense of a season. Besides, Major Henlow and my aunt are not equipped to arrange such a thing. They don't move in fashionable circles. Indeed, except for this extraordinary so-called friendship with her son, I cannot imagine Ellis contriving to get himself invited to Lady Waldemar's at all.'

'Ellis being Major Henlow's son?'

'Yes.' Clementina's face hardened. 'And a more hateful, unprincipled——' She broke off hastily. 'But that is nothing to the purpose.'

Jake was watching her intently, one of his hands curling unconsciously into a fist.

'Would it not have been more to the purpose,' he suggested slowly, 'for this *hateful* cousin of yours to sue for your hand in marriage?'

Clementina's eyes flashed. 'Marry Ellis? I would rather die!'

The contempt was unmistakable. A barely suppressed sigh escaped Jake, and his hand relaxed again. Evidently Clementina was not in love with young Henlow. His experience of women had led him always to be suspicious when they railed against a man. But then, Clementina was unlike any other female he had ever met. He ought to have realised, he reflected, that she was too direct to be capable of that sort of duplicity.

'Yet you were willing to ally yourself to the simpleton?' he said, his tone more mild. 'I repeat. What possible purpose could this serve the Henlows?'

Clementina shrugged. 'A little reflection and I must have seen it at the time. Jeremy cannot possibly live on his own, even with a wife to mind him. I had thought at first that they just wished to off-load the burden on to me. It was not such a great matter. I would have taken on Jeremy willingly enough, for it would have given me my home back again. And—and my old governess could have lived with me, for she is too old to seek another situation, and I did so want to see her settled.'

Jake's mouth twisted. 'And for such small reward you would have taken on the burden of nursemaid to a man who could give you nothing in return. Not even children.'

To his surprise, Clementina's green eyes blazed at him in sudden fury. She rose abruptly from her chair.

'You sound *exactly* like Ellis. Oh, you arrogant men! You are all the same. You think a woman cannot be satisfied unless she has a—a *man* to—to give her *p-pleasure*, as you choose to call it. I will have you know, my lord Sothern, that I am no Lady Matilda Ingleby! I don't care if I *never* have children. And—and as for a *lover*, I hope I have more respect for Jeremy than to humiliate him so!'

Jake rose, too, gazing with undisguised astonishment into the green eyes, which were luminous with unshed tears.

'But what in Hades have I said to provoke such an outburst?' he asked wonderingly. 'My dear child...'

'I am not your *dear child*!' raged Clementina. 'Not yours, not Major Henlow's. And nothing will prevail upon me to cuckold Jeremy with Ellis! *Nothing!*' With which, she burst into a paroxysm of sobs.

Enlightenment dawned on the Earl. So that was it! Not content with marrying her to a half-wit, they sought to make her Ellis Henlow's mistress. By which means, he must suppose, her acquiescence in all their schemes was to be bought. How very convenient! To have all the advantages of matrimony with none of the ties. They would have Dunhythe and its estates, and whatever fortune came with Clementina. Doubtless some plot was already afoot to declare this boy Jeremy of unsound mind, and thus gain the administration of the estates. Small wonder Clementina had run away!

While these thoughts revolved in his head he was moving, and he had enfolded the weeping girl in his arms almost before he came to the end of them. She did not resist him and he held her close, stroking her hair.

'Don't cry, Clementina,' he murmured softly. 'There is no need for all this distress. You are quite safe now. Come, look at me!' He lifted her face, and smiled down into the drowned eyes. 'I promise you there is no further cause for alarm.'

'Th-that's all v-very well,' uttered Clementina brokenly, 'but you c-can't know that.'

'Oh, yes, I can. Ellis Henlow and his father will not dare to harm you again. For you see, my sweet Clementina, you are going to marry me.'

* * *

The tears were arrested. Clementina gaped at him. Then she found her voice.

'Marry *you*? You must be mad!'

Jake grinned. 'We'll see that.'

His free hand caressed her cheek. Then his lips came down on hers. Gently, so gently, that she could barely feel them at first. Unconsciously she sighed and closed her eyes. The pressure of his lips increased. A warm glow radiated slowly through her body. Weak-kneed, she sagged in his arms, suddenly helpless. Jake held her closer still as his mouth probed hers.

A sound behind them startled Jake into full awareness. Abruptly, he let Clementina go and whirled to face the door. It was the landlord, goggling, as if unsure whether his eyes had deceived him.

'What do you want?' snapped Sothern.

'Beggin' yer honour's pardon, my lad is back from the smithy with yer honour's horse. I thought you'd wish to know, yer honour.'

'Thank you,' Jake said curtly. He glanced at Clementina's white face. She had almost fallen when he released her, and she was standing half bowed over the back of a chair, gripping it with both hands.

'You need not wait,' Jake told the landlord, who was watching her with open curiosity. 'My friend is a little faint, that is all.'

As an explanation it left much to be desired, but it would have to do, he thought, as the landlord retreated, not without a backward glance. He looked at Clementina.

'I beg your pardon. That was extremely stupid of me, with you dressed like that. I forgot myself for a moment.'

Clementina did not look at him. She pulled out a chair and sank into it. 'It is of no consequence,' she said faintly.

She was aware of Jake watching her in frowning silence as she tried to gather her thoughts together. They were chaotic. She had not known that she could be so overset by a man's caress. A wild desire had come over her to fling her arms about his neck and return his embrace. Yet this was Jake. A man many years her senior, a world apart. A man she had known but a few short days. Part of her wanted to cry out, '*Yes!* Yes, I will marry you!' But native caution and her own strong practicality held her silent. What had moved Jake to this quixotic proposal? Pity? He had spoken no words of love. He had said before that he felt responsibility for her. Was that it? She drew a steadying breath, and looked him in the eye.

'Is not such a measure a little extreme, my lord? Any responsibility you feel for me cannot possibly demand so great a sacrifice.'

Puzzled, and a little hurt, Sothern took refuge in that supercilious lift of one eyebrow. 'Of that you may leave me to be the judge.'

The green eyes flashed. 'Oh, I may, may I? And I suppose I am to have no say in the matter? No, indeed. How stupid of me! You did not *ask* me to marry you. You informed me that I was going to marry you. To be sure, I don't know why I should have expected anything different, so used as you are to having your own way with women.'

'I thought you wanted a way out of your difficulties,' Jake remarked, with an assumption of indifference.

'Yes. Escape from one tyranny into another, I thank you,' Clementina said scathingly.

'What cause have I given you to think me tyrannical?' demanded Jake with asperity, his control slipping.

'What cause? From the moment we met you have tried by every means to order my life as you think fit.'

'Well, for sheer ingratitude——'

'How dare you! What have I to be grateful for?'

'A good deal, my girl. But for my intervention you would have landed in Bow Street, for one thing. For another, I could as easily have taken advantage of you as have introduced you to my grandmother.'

'You flatter yourself, my lord! Don't think I would have hesitated to hit you on the head with that candlestick!'

'Oh, for God's sake!' Jake ejaculated impatiently. 'This is a singularly stupid argument. I have offered a way out of your dilemma. If you don't wish to avail yourself of it you have only to say so.'

'I *don't* wish to. I had by far rather marry Jeremy!' Clementina announced, and sat regarding him balefully.

Sothern compressed his lips on a sharp retort. He poured himself out another glass of wine and tossed it off.

'Very well,' he said with forced calm as he put down the glass. 'What do you intend to do now?'

Clementina looked away. 'I don't know.'

'You had better think, then.'

'I won't do so with you standing over me like a hawk!' she snapped.

'I beg your pardon,' he said stiffly, and sat down on the other side of the table.

Silence reigned for some few moments. Then Clementina stole a glance at Sothern and found him watching her. Involuntarily her lips quivered on a smile. In seconds they were both laughing.

'You bring out the worst in me, you know,' Clementina told him cheerfully.

'Permit me to return the compliment,' Jake grinned with a mock bow. 'Now that the civilities are in order let us consider what to do.'

Clementina grimaced. 'I was going to Dunhythe, but sooner or later they will find me there.'

'Does that matter? I mean, if you seriously mean to go through with this marriage.'

'I do,' Clementina stated firmly. 'But I have to find a way to protect Dunhythe—and Jeremy, if it comes to that.'

'I don't see how you can do so. If you were of age you could get a power of attorney from him once he was your husband. But as it stands——'

'That is it!' she exclaimed. 'I will lay the whole matter before Mr Cullen. He will find some legal way to set matters to rights. Or at least to make sure the rewards of Papa's good management do not fall into the wrong hands.'

Lord Sothern said nothing for a moment. Privately he doubted whether there was much Cullen could do, but that was not why he hesitated. All this felt unreal. There should be no need for Cullen's services, no need of Clementina's devising ways and means to marry a simpleton and keep their joint inheritance out of the hands of schemers. What did feel real was the idea that Clementina belonged to him. As if to clear it he shook his head a little. Absurd! There was no question of it. She had refused him in no uncertain terms. But the curious feeling persisted.

'Then if you are determined on this course,' he said at last, in a voice that did not seem to belong to him, 'I will escort you back to London.'

Since he had not brought his groom with him on what might prove to be a somewhat delicate mission, Sothern was glad that the runaway had elected to travel as a male. It obviated the need for a chaperon, and made it acceptable for him to convey them both to London in his phaeton. Clementina's hired horse was tethered to run behind until they could find a posting-house from where it could be officially conveyed back to its stable in London.

For the first few miles there was relative silence in the phaeton, with both seemingly occupied with their own thoughts. There was, too, a certain measure of reserve which had built up through the luncheon they had swiftly consumed at the Little Foxes.

The Earl, glancing round at his companion, found himself strangely affected by the sight of her in men's clothing, reminding him irresistibly of the night they had met.

'Where did you get that hat?' he asked, his eyebrow flying, referring to the small-brimmed beaver perched at a jaunty angle over her red-gold locks. 'It makes you the very devil of a fellow!'

Her lips quivered, and she twinkled up at him. 'It is not what you said of me that night.'

'*That* night? Why, no. But then I did not know with what a spirited adventurer I had to deal.' He smiled. 'Perhaps I did, though. Only I had not yet recognised the fact.'

Clementina bit her lip. 'I am not truly spirited. Had I been, I should have taken a pistol to that hateful man!'

'I thank God you were not, then,' Jake said, laughing. 'I should have hated to have met you only to see you swing at Tyburn.'

She looked at him with interest. 'Do you tell me you have no power to prevent such a thing?'

'Good God, child, I am not a magician! Do you imagine a peer of the realm to be outside the law?'

'N-no,' she replied consideringly, 'but he must have a good deal of influence within it.'

'Shrewdly judged. But I beg you will not attempt murder in the hopes that I may be able to get you off!'

Clementina laughed. 'I did not mean that. I was only thinking how different it all is in your world.'

He shrugged. 'Not so very. I dare say you would soon find yourself at home were you to take up residence in London.'

'God forbid!' Clementina ejaculated.

Taken aback, he glanced down at her. 'Was it so very bad these few days?'

'Quite dreadful!' she confirmed without hesitation. 'To be so stared at and talked of, and—and all to provide entertainment for a set of idle persons who have nothing better to do.'

'And what would you find to do of more interest,' he asked coolly, though with a touch of hauteur, 'married to your simpleton cousin, and stuck in your rural retreat from one year's end to the other?'

'Plenty.' She paused. 'At least—well, to be sure, there is not *that* much employment. Apart from—from keeping house and—and managing the estate, I suppose. But—but I always found a lot to do,' she went on, almost pleadingly, unaware that she had fallen to reminiscing rather than imagining a future life. 'I—I rode, and read, and there were games to keep us amused. Bowls on the lawn. Shuttlecock and battledore.' She laughed. 'Poor Margery could never get in the way of it, so I always won. Then there were the assemblies at Norwich. We visited with our friends, of course, and—and there was Jeremy, too. Papa was used often to ask him for a visit, for he knew Major Henlow did not care for him. Besides, Jeremy was his heir. He always said he should have married again, but he never did. Mama died, you see, after I was born. I suppose he never bothered because for some years my aunt lived with us and kept house. Then she married the vicar and Margery came as governess to me, and *she* kept house, too. Though indeed it was not supposed to be part of her duties.'

'Is that where you were going for refuge, to your aunt?' asked Jake, his interest in these revelations having completely obliterated the annoyance he had felt at the slight to the milieu in which he moved.

'Oh, no. Aunt Fanny died. She was the one who had all those still-born children, you know. Besides, they moved away when her husband was given a much better living in Yorkshire. We had not seen either of them for years, though he wrote to me on Papa's death, of course.'

'So there really is no one. No one at all?' Jake sounded incredulous.

There was a far-away look in her eyes as she glanced up. As if she did not see him. As if her mind was still back with the memories.

'There is Margery. Margery Plumstead, my governess, you must know. She is keeping house until—until something may be settled.'

'You love your home very much, I take it.'

Clementina shrugged. 'Yes and no. One's home must always be full of memories, I suppose. It is not that so much. It—it is only that—that Papa and I——' She broke off, swallowing on her distress, but her voice continued husky. 'We were very f-fond, you see. We were the closest of companions. Papa was apt to treat me a little as if I had been a son. He—he taught me to enjoy things that—that perhaps a young lady is not meant to do.'

'What things?' Jake asked softly.

'Oh, riding for one.' She blushed a little, but there was a quiver of the lips on the next word. *'Astride.'*

'Oh, my God!'

'Yes. Breeches, you see, are scarcely new to me. I always borrowed Jeremy's, as it happens. Indeed, this is an old suit of his.'

The Earl's lips were twitching uncontrollably. 'And what else did this admirably innovative father of yours see fit to teach you?'

Clementina giggled. 'Nothing very startling, in all honesty. We fished the trout stream together, and he did try to teach me to handle a gun, but I had no aim. And try as I would I could not help but jump and squeak with shock at the explosion. So he gave it up.' She added, with an air of making up for this deficiency, 'But I proved adept at cards and chess, and could give him a lead when it came to port after dinner!'

It was too much. Lord Sothern collapsed with laughter, dropping his hands so that his team gave a sudden forward lurch and he was obliged to attend to what he was doing to bring them back under control.

'I wish I might handle a team,' Clementina commented wistfully, watching his expertise with some envy. 'Though I can control a pair without quite disgracing Papa.'

'I will teach you,' Jake replied easily, quite forgetting what had earlier passed between them, 'when we are married.'

Clementina jerked bolt upright, snapping hastily, 'We are not going to be married!'

Sothern reddened as everything came flooding back. What the devil had possessed him? He must be out of his mind!

'As you say,' he said at his most bland.

But the barriers were up again. Tension reigned with renewed silence until at length they reached the first main posting-house on the London road.

Sothern's first move was to get rid of Clementina's hired horse. While he was arranging for its conveyance back to London Clementina looked for a chambermaid to direct her where she might use the conveniences of the house.

Recalling her unconventional dress in time, however, she beckoned instead to one of the male servants, and found herself being led through the busy inn and out into the back courtyard. As she approached the water-closet a youth came out of it and she stopped short.

'Dear Lord! Jeremy!' she exclaimed before she could stop herself.

The young man jumped, backed hurriedly, and then stood staring with his mouth hanging wide. He was a gangling youth, rather thin, with a gaunt look about the face. Only his eyes, vacant under a protruding brow, belied the appearance of age. He was, in fact, some six and twenty years old, but the gawky awkwardness of his stance, the hunching of his shoulders, and the inability to hold his head fully erect made him seem little more than an adolescent.

'C-Clemmy?' he said in a mystified tone, unable to equate this young man with the face of his cousin.

Clementina hurried up to him, and urgently grasped his arm. 'Yes, yes, it is I. But what are you doing here, Jeremy? Where is my aunt? Don't tell me they have brought you without her?'

'C-Clemmy?' he said again.

'Yes, Jeremy, I really am Clemmy,' she told him more slowly, realising his confusion. 'Now, where is your mama?'

He still stared stupidly. Clementina shook his arm.

'Jeremy, answer me. Where is your mama?'

'In the c-carriage,' he stammered slowly, his gaze still riveted on his cousin's attire. The idea finally surfaced. 'My-my suit, Clemmy.'

'Yes, it is your suit, Jeremy. I thought you would not mind if I borrowed it.'

'Don't m-mind. Not for *you*, C-Clemmy.'

She squeezed his arm. 'I knew you would not. Now tell me, Jeremy. Is your brother with you? And my uncle?'

He shook his head slowly. 'G-gone.'

'Gone where?'

Jeremy shook his head again. 'N-not in the c-carriage.'

'No, very well. But where have they gone? To Dunhythe?'

'D-Dunhythe is m-mine.'

'Yes, Dunhythe is yours,' agreed Clementina, controlling her natural impatience. 'But has your papa gone there?'

'D-don't know. N-not in the carriage,' he repeated, sticking to the one idea of which he was certain.

Clementina gave it up. She had to find out if Major Henlow was at Dunhythe. There was only one way to do so. 'Take me to the carriage, Jeremy. To your mama.'

Propelling him forward, she urged him on with the same request repeated several times. Grasping her intention, Jeremy then led her quite quickly into the inn yard where there was a bustle of carriages and passengers, with ostlers and grooms leading horses to and from the shafts, and waiters scurrying with trays of cakes and wine to slake the thirst of parched travellers.

Clementina saw her aunt's face peering anxiously from the window of a large coach. It was easy to see from where Ellis got his looks, although his mother's beauty was rather faded now. Her elder son favoured his deceased father.

Mrs Henlow saw Jeremy, but did not immediately connect the fair stripling who accompanied her with her errant niece.

'Jeremy, at last! I had begun to worry. Come inside, quickly.' Then she recognised her niece and gave a small shriek. *'Clementina!'*

'Hush, aunt!' Clementina whispered fiercely. 'Don't call me by name, for heaven's sake!'

'But, my dear child, how come you here? And dressed like that?'

'Never mind that now. It is too long a story. Is my uncle with you? And Ellis?'

'No, no, they have gone in search of you.' Mrs Henlow opened the coach door on the words, and instructed her son to get in.

Jeremy stood his ground. 'C-Clemmy come?'

'Yes, yes, of course Clemmy will come,' his mother said soothingly. 'You had better get in, my dear. You know what he is.'

Clementina hesitated. 'Yes, but I am not coming with you, aunt. I have an escort, you know. I am going back to London.'

'Oh, my love, you will do precisely as you wish. But do get in just for a moment. Otherwise I may never get him back in at all.'

Reluctantly Clementina climbed into the coach, knowing well how stubborn her simple cousin could be.

'That is better,' said Mrs Henlow comfortably, as she watched her son clamber in and take his seat next to his cousin. 'Now, you will tell me all about it as we go.'

'What?' gasped Clementina.

In a flash she was up, grabbing for the door handle.

'Hold Clemmy, Jeremy,' her aunt ordered shrilly. *'Hold her.* Do you hear me? Hold her tight!'

Obediently the youth seized Clementina about the waist and pulled her back against him.

'Let me go, Jeremy!' she cried furiously. 'Let go!'

In his confusion Jeremy held her tighter, while the two women shouted conflicting instructions. In the midst of the commotion Mrs Henlow seized her parasol from the seat beside her and rapped on the roof. Clementina struggled madly in her cousin's strong grip as the coach began ponderously to move.

Frantic now, Clementina beat her fists behind her at Jeremy's body. 'Let me go, you idiot! *Let me go!* Aunt, you will regret this!'

Becoming frightened, Jeremy slackened his hold. Seeing it, his mother lifted her parasol and delivered a cracking blow to Clementina's head.

For a second the green eyes stared in horrified disbelief. Then the lashes fluttered over them and she sank limply into unconsciousness.

CHAPTER SEVEN

JAKE grew steadily more impatient. They had eaten a luncheon before leaving the Little Foxes where he had found Clementina, and there was no reason for delay. There was a crisp wind blowing, and he feared it might come on to rain. Besides, he was anxious to get her back under his grandmother's roof where he could more readily discuss her situation in an atmosphere of calm. A wayside inn was no place to try to persuade a determined young lady to give up a scheme so disastrous to her happiness. Between the three of them he trusted that Cullen, the dowager and himself must be able to accomplish a change of mind.

But as the minutes passed and Clementina put in no appearance anxiety began to gnaw at him. Uneasily recalling the end of their last conversation, he could not but wonder if his careless remark had been taken seriously. The fear that Clementina had run away from him again could not but enter his mind.

He went out into the yard just in case she should be waiting in the phaeton. She was not there, and the ostler who held his horses had not seen her. About to weave his way back through the several carriages thronging the yard, the Earl heard himself hailed from behind.

'Jake, old fellow! Just the man we're looking for.'

Turning, Sothern saw his friend, Sir Harry Blaine, just dismounting, and Theo Farleigh, still on horseback and waving his whip. Both men were generously dust-spattered, their horses in a lather of sweat.

'My God!' Jake ejaculated. 'What are you two doing here?'

'Her ladyship sent us after you,' Sir Harry responded, giving his horse into the charge of a groom. 'By God, what a chase! I could do with a gallon of ale, by God I could!'

'Do you mean my grandmother sent you?'

'Well, it wasn't Maud, old fellow, I can tell you that.'

'But why?' demanded Sothern, mystified.

'All in good time, my friend. All in good time. Wet my whistle first, or I won't get the words out.'

Sir Harry stomped off in the direction of the taproom, but Farleigh had come up with them by now, and he laid a hand on Sothern's shoulder.

'Your young lady's guardian turned up, Jake,' he said in a low tone. 'Lady Staplegrove sent us to tell you that the man and his son are on their way to this place, Dunhythe. What's more, they think you're escorting Clementina. Have you found her, by the by?'

'I had,' Jake replied, 'but I very much fear she may have given me the slip again.'

They pushed their way after Sir Harry Blaine into the busy inn, and over a jug or two of ale his friends told Sothern of Major Henlow's visit to his grandmother. In return Jake explained how he had come to find Clementina, and the reason for his still being at this particular hostelry.

'But if she meant to go to your man Cullen, why should she run off again?' Blaine asked. 'Ain't as if you was any danger to her.'

Sothern refrained from telling his friends the one reason why he feared Clementina might wish to escape him.

'And where would she go?' added Theo. 'She won't see Cullen tonight, and she must sleep somewhere.'

Jake frowned. 'You're right. It doesn't make sense. I had better see what I can find out.'

'Why?' he was demanding half an hour later, as they all stood in the back yard of the inn. 'This makes even less sense than ever.'

A waiter and no less than two ostlers and a groom had seen Clementina with a young man in the inn yard. She had entered a coach of her own free will and it had driven away towards the north. More puzzling still, the description of the other man did not tally with that of Ellis Henlow as supplied by Lady Staplegrove, nor with what both Blaine and Sothern recalled of him.

'Beggin' your honour's pardon,' interrupted the waiter, grinning, 'but it's t'other gennelman as made no sense.'

Jake bent a frowning gaze upon the man. 'What do you mean?'

'Touched in his upper works, if you arst me, your honour,' said the waiter. 'C-couldn't h-hardly speak without s-stammering hisself to p-pieces,' he mimicked, making the ostlers and the groom laugh.

'And I seen him stood there, a-gaping like a noddy, when your young gennelman speaks to 'im, your honour.'

Sothern had heard enough. He distributed coins among the servants, and led his friends back into the inn.

'One thing is clear. She has gone with her cousin, Sir Jeremy Hythe.'

'What, the stammerer?' demanded Blaine.

'The poor boy is a half-wit,' Jake explained. 'Clementina intends to marry him.'

'You must be joking!' Theo exclaimed, shocked. 'She *could* not do so.'

'She won't, if I have anything to say to it,' Jake promised grimly. 'We must act fast. Obviously they are headed for Dunhythe. Equally obviously, Clementina does not know that the Henlows are following. I cannot tell whether we are before or behind that pair, but I suspect the latter. Now, Harry, you and I will go on to Norfolk.'

'Whatever you say,' Blaine agreed equably. 'As long as there's a decent inn and a good meal to be had.'

'We'll find you one,' Sothern promised. 'Theo, I want you to go back to London. Hire another horse. I'll see that both yours and Harry's get back safe to town. There is no time to be lost. I've a strong feeling I might need something important, and I want you to fetch it for me.'

Theo sighed. 'I'm to ride to the devil and back in no time, is that it?'

Jake grinned. 'Tomorrow will do. They can't do much harm in what little there is left of the day.

And that's all the chance they are going to get, trust me!'

Darkness had long fallen by the time the travellers reached Lodeton, to which small Norfolk town Mr Cullen had directed Lord Sothern. Settled comfortably at the Red Lion, and with a good dinner inside them, Jake then dragged Sir Harry Blaine from his cognac to go in search of the little village some few miles distant which served the estate of the late Sir Clement Hythe.

The Bear was the single small inn at Dunhythe, and its genial host, Mr Huxtable, was gratified to be hailed by name by the London swell who had entered the place on this late April evening. When he learned that Mr Cullen—'as good a man as ever stepped'—had commended his house to Lord Sothern, he expanded visibly and was drawn out with ease on the subject of Dunhythe and its inmates.

'A big day it be, with the new squire coming home to roost, m'lord.'

'That would be Sir Jeremy, I take it?'

'Aye, Sir Jeremy that be, poor lad. For he's a nice enough young man, for all he's missing half his wits.'

Jake probed gently, and learned that Sir Jeremy had arrived with his mother, setting all in a bustle up at the house, by all Mr Huxtable could discover. For scarcely had they been settled when Mrs Henlow's husband had turned up with her other son, Mr Ellis. Miss Margery had been in a rare taking by what the footman had said when he'd come down the village for supplies.

'Miss Margery?' enquired Sothern, brows raised.

'Aye, Margery Plumstead, that be, m'lord. She as was governess to Miss Clementina. Well, more like a housekeeper these last months, looking after the place until Sir Jeremy should take it into his head to come and live there.'

Unable to contain himself, Sir Harry rapped on the table. 'And Miss Clementina? What of her, man? Did she...?'

Sothern's warning hand on his arm stopped him, and Jake intervened. 'You were saying, Huxtable?'

The landlord looked from one to the other with puzzled eyes. 'Funny that be, you asking after Miss Clementina, sir. I thought she'd be with them, sure, for the banns has been posted more than three weeks now.'

A cold hand gripped Jake's heart. 'Banns?'

'Aye, m'lord. Though not one o' we expected as how Sir Jeremy and Miss Clementina would make a match of it.'

Sothern paled. Seeing it, Blaine gripped his arm and drew him a little apart.

'By God, Jake, what's to do?' he demanded in a lowered tone. 'If the girl ain't there what the dickens are they playing at?'

'It's what they had planned all along,' Jake answered quietly. 'Clementina would have complied but for one circumstance. I know she would not agree willingly without seeing Cullen to arrange something first.'

'Riddles, riddles!' exclaimed Sir Harry impatiently. 'Is she with them or no? That's all you have to find out.'

Jake shook his head. 'It is not all. But it's the first priority.' Swiftly he stepped back to the landlord. 'Listen, Huxtable, I need your help. I must get to speak with this Miss Margery you mention. Can you get a message to her, do you suppose?'

Huxtable hesitated. But as Jake brought out his purse his eyes glistened and he licked his lips and winked. 'Nothing easier, m'lord.'

'Good. Then ask her to meet me here early to-morrow. Tell her it is vital to Miss Clementina's happiness.'

Intrigued, but highly delighted with the gold coins that slipped from his lordship's palm to his own, the landlord promised to do as he was bid.

After a restless night Sothern returned alone to the Bear in the early hours, leaving Sir Harry asleep. He found awaiting him not Margery Plumstead, but Sir Jeremy Hythe.

'I be that sorry, m'lord,' apologised the landlord, 'but Sir Jeremy says as how Miss Margery sent him.'

The gangling youth was staring at the newcomer round-eyed from under his protruding brow. As Sothern approached him he backed a little.

'Come, there is no need to be afraid of me,' Jake said kindly, holding a hand. 'I am a friend of Clementina's, you know.'

'C-Clemmy?' Jeremy managed, and extended his own hand.

'Yes,' Jake affirmed, shaking the hand briefly. 'Do you know where she is?' And, when no response was forthcoming, 'Clemmy. Where is she?'

'C-Clemmy's going to m-marry me,' the youth announced proudly.

Jake clenched his teeth. Oh, no, she is not, he thought. Poor devil! What did this boy know of marriage? Of what it would mean to Clementina? He changed tack.

'Margery gave you a message for me, I believe.'

Jeremy nodded. 'M-Margery said to c-come. She c-can't.'

'What did she want you to tell me?'

The youth frowned in an effort of memory. 'She s-said—she s-said——'

'Take your time,' Jake urged gently. 'What did Margery say?'

'Margery s-said she must s-stay with C-Clemmy.'

Then she was there! A sigh escaped Jake. Now he must get the boy to help him. It was a base trick to serve him, getting him to queer his own pitch. But that could not be helped.

'Listen, Jeremy,' he said slowly, 'if I give you a note, will you take it to Clemmy?'

'C-can't,' the youth said positively. 'C-can't see Clemmy. C-Clemmy l-locked up.'

Gingerly, Clementina's fingers probed the bruise on the side of her head. The swelling had subsided a little, but it was still tender to the touch. The blinding headache that had prevented her from thinking at all last night had dulled to a monotonous background pain. Had it not been for Margery's presence, she reflected thankfully, she might have lost her senses entirely. The old governess had clucked over her as she'd applied cold compresses to the wound. She had made a tisane and obliged Clementina to drink it so that she slept for most of the night.

The key grated in the lock, and Margery Plumstead herself came in, bearing a tray covered with a cloth.

'Ah, you are awake, my pet,' she cried joyfully, coming to the bed. 'And how do you feel this morning?'

Clementina gave her a wan smile. 'Better.' She looked at the tray. 'I hope you have brought something to eat. I'm famished.'

Margery laid the tray down and removed the cloth. 'Bread and butter, a baked egg, tea, and a lardy cake,' she announced, smiling.

'Oh, wonderful!' exclaimed Clementina, seizing upon a slice of bread.

The governess fetched a shawl from one of the drawers of the dresser and laid it around the girl's shoulders. She looked on fondly as her erstwhile charge satisfied her immediate hunger.

She was a desiccated female of some sixty years, thin and sallow, with greying mousy hair strictly confined under an unbecoming cap, clad in an old stuff gown that hung loosely on her scarecrow body. But her pale grey eyes were kindly, and her manner towards Clementina was warm with a very real affection.

She sat on the bed and leaned forward. 'There is something I must tell you, my pet,' she said in conspiratorial tones.

Her mouth full, Clementina only looked a question.

'There is someone come to Dunhythe to see you—secretly. At least, he does not wish his presence known to the Henlows.'

Clementina's breath caught. 'Jake?' she whispered.

'Is that his name? Huxtable told me only that he was a lord.'

'Lord Sothern,' Clementina confirmed, hastily laying down the cake she had been eating. 'Where is he?'

'I don't know, my pet. I was to meet him at the Bear this morning. But I did not care to leave you, so I sent Master Jeremy. Besides, it would have been difficult to find an excuse to quit my post.'

Clementina sank back against the pillows. 'You will have to go, Margery. Jeremy will never make Sothern understand that I must escape, for he thinks we are to be married.'

The governess regarded her with pitying eyes. 'But so does everyone think it, Clemmy. The banns have been read these three Sundays in St Mark's. You wrote to tell me yourself of your plans. It was only when they locked you up last night I began to wonder—although your aunt said it was a punishment for running away and wearing gentleman's clothing. Though why they should punish you when you had been hurt so in that accident I'm sure I don't know.'

Clementina shook her head. 'Oh, Margie, it was no accident. You know it was not.'

Margery pursed her lips. 'Now, Clemmy, my pet, you are not going to start again with all those taradiddles, are you? As if your dear aunt would

dream of raising a hand to you, let alone hitting
you with her parasol! I never heard of such a thing!
All very well to talk such nonsense last night when
you were not yourself,' she said severely, 'but this
morning it is quite another matter.'

'Margie, you must believe me!' Clementina
urged, sitting up and seizing the governess's hands.
'You *do* believe me! Why else would you have told
me Jake had come here?'

A slight blush mantled the governess's faded
cheek. 'To tell you the truth, my pet, I suspected
at once. You need not hide your feelings from me.
You have fallen in love, have you not? That is why
you ran away! I guessed it, you see. And then when
I received a message from this lord I was sure of
it. Tell me the whole, Clemmy. I never did like the
idea of your marrying Master Jeremy, and if this
gentleman is not wholly ineligible—which, if he is
indeed a lord, I do not see how he can be,
unless——'

'Oh, Margery, stop!' begged Clementina. 'You
have it all wrong. I shall have to tell you the whole
story.'

But, before she could say anything more, the door
opened and Mrs Henlow entered the room.

'Good morning, Clementina,' she said pleasantly. 'Miss Plumstead, leave us, if you please. I
wish to talk to my niece alone.'

The governess rose hastily and left the room, only
throwing a glance at her charge that was meant to
convey reassurance. Seeing with what alacrity
Margery obeyed her aunt, Clementina's spirits sank.
She recalled that the governess was only here on

sufferance, for the house belonged to Jeremy, and she could be turned out of it at the Henlows' pleasure. Small wonder poor Margery was only too eager to please! There was little hope, then, that she could be—or even ought to be—persuaded to help get Clementina out of Dunhythe.

'I am glad to see you looking more like yourself, my dear,' Mrs Henlow said in a tone of kindness, coming to the bed.

'No thanks to you!' Clementina snapped.

Her aunt sighed. 'Do not think I took any pleasure in hurting you, my poor child. Indeed, it was only the direst necessity that compelled me to take such a drastic measure.'

'I suppose I should thank God that you had not a pistol about you,' Clementina said sarcastically.

'Oh, no. How could you think it? Your death would not serve us in the very least.'

'How lucky for me!'

'Dear child, you are talking nonsense, and no wonder. You are obviously still rather unwell. Now that is a pity, for the wedding is arranged for this afternoon.'

Clementina sat bolt upright. *'What?'*

Mrs Henlow smiled. 'We thought there was little point in delay.'

'I won't do it,' Clementina said flatly.

Her aunt sat on the bed, sighing again. Like her husband, she was dressed some years behind the times, even a little shabbily, the cloth riding-habit she was wont to wear by day a trifle threadbare. It was plain that every penny was squandered on her beloved son.

'I am afraid you must do it, dear child,' she continued. 'You see, our affairs are in a sad way. We did not quite like to burden you with all this, but I am afraid that if we cannot settle our debts the bailiffs will descend upon our house in Rye in a matter of days. Not that it is our house, of course, mortgaged as it is right up to the hilt.'

'I had not realised things were as bad as that,' Clementina said, frowning. 'What was Mr Henlow about, to bring things to such a pass?'

'Oh, it is not all John's fault, poor man,' said her aunt, sighing again. 'It is my dear but reckless Ellis. He loves to live high. And why should he not?'

'Perhaps because he has not the means,' suggested Clementina evenly.

'Now he has not, no. But he will. Luckily, he is a sensible boy, and made friends to some purpose at Oxford. He has already made headway in the fashionable set. Now with the security of this place and the revenue from the estates that will come from your share——'

'But I am not marrying Ellis, ma'am.'

'No, indeed, that I would never permit!' said Mrs Henlow in shocked tones. 'Why, Ellis is so extremely handsome, it would surprise me if he does not catch a title in addition to the heiress I am certain he must secure.'

Clementina drew a breath. 'I see. So I am to be the sacrifice to oil Ellis Henlow's path.'

Ellis's besotted mother smiled brightly at her. 'Why, Clementina, that is it in a nutshell. I confess I cannot see why you should object. You will have your home, and you need have nothing to do with my poor Jeremy if you do not wish it. And although one should not speak of such things, of course, there is no point in missishness now. Ellis,' she said delicately, 'is perfectly willing to make up for the obvious defects of his brother.'

'Oh, be quiet, Aunt! I wonder you are not ashamed to own knowledge of that!'

'In the ordinary way I should be, naturally. But we are females together, and quite alone. It must be admitted that a personable lover is no small compensation to a neglected wife.'

'Doubtless you speak from experience!' flashed Clementina.

'Indeed, no. But allow me some feeling for you, my dear. I do sincerely pity you, situated as you are.'

'Fiddle! You do not think of me at all, or you would see for yourself how revolted I must be by such an arrangement. I am truly sorry for your financial difficulties, but I tell you now that nothing you can say or do will induce me to marry Jeremy under these conditions. Indeed, after your brutal conduct to me yesterday, I am not of a mind to marry him at all!'

There was a moment's pause while Mrs Henlow eyed her consideringly. Then she sighed once more and rose.

'I am sorry that you have taken up so intransigent an attitude. I had hoped you would acquiesce like a sensible girl. I regret that it will now be up to John and Ellis to use what methods they deem necessary to force you to submit.'

She waited a moment for the implications of her words to sink in. But although Clementina paled a little she met her aunt's look with a defiant stare and her chin up, and said not a word.

With a final small sigh Mrs Henlow turned on her heel and left the room. The key clicked in the lock, and Clementina was left to her own reflections. They were not happy ones.

In spite of her brave words she was beginning to feel hopelessly trapped. If only she had not seen Jeremy yesterday! If Jake had not left her briefly alone in order to arrange about the horse.

This idea brought a lump to her throat. Sothern had come after her, had tried to get in contact with her. Surely that must mean more than the cold ring of that word 'responsibility'. And he had kissed her! Only, with Jake that did not mean anything. She must suppose that a man of his reputed success with the ladies would know well enough how to make his caresses acceptable. It had not, in the past, unless rumour lied, betokened anything more than a passing fancy for any woman. Well, Clementina Hythe was not going to figure in any man's gallery of past conquests. Nor would she give in and lend herself to the disgraceful proposal outlined by her aunt Henlow!

The thought brought the present reality crashing in on her. Small comfort to recall Jake's kiss, when there was nothing he could do now to save her. Margery had sent Jeremy to him. That in itself must spell disaster. Whatever poor Jeremy found to say could only alienate Jake's sympathies. Besides, she had expressly and strongly stated to Jake that she would marry Jeremy. When he heard of the arrangements for the wedding, would he not suppose that she had agreed, and wash his hands of her?

A solitary tear squeezed its way from the corner of her eye and stole down her cheek. Clementina angrily brushed it away, sternly admonishing herself. *Idiot.* This was no way to save herself. She must think! Think and act.

The sound of the key in the lock startled her. For a craven moment she knew blind panic, and her heart began to hammer with fear. But it was only Margery. Relief flooded through her, and she re-laxed back against her pillows as the governess came hurrying to the bed.

'Oh, my poor Clemmy! You are as white as a sheet. What is it, my dear?'

Clementina shook her head, but urgently grasped the governess's hand. 'Nothing, nothing. Only tell me! Have you seen Jeremy? Has he spoken with Jake?'

'Alas, my pet! He was seized upon by the Major as soon as ever he came back. I believe they are rehearsing him in his part. For the ceremony in the church, you know.'

'Oh, dear Lord!' Clementina burst out. 'There is no escape! None. Unless—Margie, you must go to Jake.'

'But, my love, I——'

'Please, Margie! I don't know what he can do, but he must be told that I am forced into this mar-riage against my will. I beg of you——'

She broke off as the door opened. Ellis Henlow stood framed in the doorway. She stared at him in some trepidation, clinging tight to Margery's hand.

That lady, quite scandalised by the appearance in her charge's bedroom of a male member of the household, began to cluck at once.

'Mr Ellis! Sir! I must beg you to retire. This is most unseemly.' She put up a hand to one blushing cheek. 'A gentleman in a lady's bedchamber!'

'Quiet, woman!' ordered Mr Henlow, calmly walking into the room.

'Sir, I will not be quiet,' daringly announced the governess, coming forward as if to stand as a screen between the man and Clementina. 'I declare, I cannot allow——'

With one violent motion of his arm Ellis swept her aside. She fell against the wall, gasping in outrage and fear. Clementina started up in the bed, green eyes fairly blazing.

'You *brute*! How could you do such a thing?'

A sneer marred the comely countenance. 'With ease, dear cousin. A pity my father did not see fit to mete out some of the same treatment to you. We might then have been spared a good deal of trouble.'

'You are the most detestable, vile-humoured man I have ever met!' Clementina threw at him. 'How I wish I had a gun! I would take infinite pleasure in blowing your head off!'

Ellis threw back his head and laughed, a chilling sound, devoid of humour. 'You are undoubtedly wasted on my brother, Clemmy. But you should not show your temper to me, you know. My rancour is infinitely worse than my pleasure. And that you may command at any time if you will only cease this futile rebellion.'

'If ever you carry out your design,' Clementina grated through set teeth, 'you will do so with my insensible body, and at no other time.'

The sneer became more marked as he leaned close. 'That could prove most interesting.'

Clementina spat—full in his face. In a flash his hand shot out, and struck her a stinging blow across the cheek.

'Ellis!' roared Major Henlow from the doorway, just as the governess rushed to her charge's side to clasp her in agitated arms.

Mr Henlow, his face livid still with fury, turned to face his parent.

'Will you control yourself, sir?' Major Henlow came swiftly to grasp his son by the arm. 'I told you, no violence,' he added, low-toned.

Ellis stepped back, his jaw clenched. Although he accepted his father's authority it was evident that he resented it. Major Henlow turned to Clementina, who pulled herself from her governess's arms to face him.

'My dear child, I must apologise for my son's rash conduct.'

'Oh, you n-need not t-trouble, sir,' Clementina said, sarcasm rife in her voice, though her lip trembled. 'I am b-becoming accustomed to the peculiar m-manners obtaining in your f-family.'

The Major's mouth hardened. 'Clementina, you do yourself no good by such observations. I promise you my intentions towards you are kindly. Strive,

I beg of you, to refrain from alienating my affections.'

'Affections?' The green eyes brightened with angry tears. 'You forget, sir, that I had a rare example to guide me as to the nature of true affection. There is no care, no love for me here.'

'Oh, my pet, how can you say so?' protested Margery, tears starting to her own eyes.

Clementina's hand went out to her. 'I don't mean you, Margie. You know I don't.'

Much gratified, the governess took the hand and held it to her cheek.

'An affecting spectacle!' remarked Ellis Henlow. 'Do you intend to wait all day for my cousin's reluctant assent, sir? Or do we take matters into our own hands?'

Major Henlow turned a stern countenance upon his step-niece. 'Clementina, once and for all, will you or will you not do as you are asked?'

There was a pause. Even Margery released the hand she held and stepped back to await the answer. Clementina drew a resolute breath and lifted her chin, her eyes steady on Major Henlow's face.

'Do your worst. For I had rather die than submit.'

CHAPTER EIGHT

IN ONE semi-lucid interval Clementina was sure that it must all be a dream. She was aware of the constant presence of Margery, and the occasional sight of the other faces: John Henlow, Ellis, her aunt, and once even Jeremy. At least the world about her had ceased to spin and topple in its giddying dance.

Coming out of the darkness that had first enveloped her, her gaze had fallen upon a nightmare confusion of strange shapes and fancied images. At least, she presumed them to be fancies. The ceiling rose high above her, distant and tiny. Then some elongated features hung over her, in which she with difficulty recognised Margery. Someone had pulled her up so that the huge form of the bedpost with its heavy drapery billowed to meet her. She had shrunk back, a cry rasping from her hoarse throat.

Voices urged her to stand, but for the life of her she could not maintain any balance on her own two feet. Or she thought she could not. But there she was, a long, thin creature framed in the fulsome expanse of the pier-glass in the corner, her stays in place and her petticoats clinging about her legs.

She felt herself falling, and clutched out for support. Hands steadied her, and she found herself gazing into the somehow bloated features of her aunt. Though she could not recall the reason, Clementina knew there was something here to fear.

She pushed away, whimpering, and, losing balance, collapsed into blessed darkness once more.

She came round again to find the room no longer swaying and changing shape before her eyes. But an immense lassitude possessed her, and it was all she could do to obey the dictates of the peremptory voice which ordered her to rise. Weak, unsteady on her feet, she was bundled into a simple gown of white muslin, her hair dressed with a fillet of artificial flowers, and her feet pushed into a pair of satin slippers.

As Margery was tenderly placing a woollen cape about her shoulders the door opened to admit Major Henlow. The sound drew Clementina's attention and she turned a wan face towards the door. At sight of her uncle a picture flashed through her mind: Margery being pushed from the room, while strong hands held Clementina's struggling form; the major crossing back to the bed, his hand sliding from his pocket with a glass phial clasped between his fingers.

Clementina raised a wavering hand to thrust the image in the doorway from her. She heard his voice. 'Is she ready? We have not much time.'

Then her aunt. 'We are quite finished. Only let me fetch my own bonnet and we may start.'

Unresisting, Clementina was led from the room, her faltering steps guided by Margery close at her side. Through the thick cloud in her mind she sought for answers to the riddles this dream was posing. She knew she had rejected this, yet here she was, acquiescent, being drawn like the sacrificial lamb to the slaughter.

Outside the house there were carriages waiting. Ellis Henlow stood at the foot of the front steps. Seeing him, Clementina halted abruptly, and let out a small sound, something like the mew of a frightened kitten.

Another image had broken through—the face of this man, curiously upside-down, one hand savagely pushing her head back, while the other held her body in a painful grip that clamped her to his chest. Liquid had been tilted down her throat. She had spluttered, choked and swallowed on a bitter taste. Thrown back on the bed, she had slipped swiftly into oblivion.

'Get in the carriage, Ellis,' her aunt's voice said urgently. 'And keep out of sight. We don't want her agitated.'

With Ellis vanished, Margery and Mrs Henlow had succeeded in pushing Clementina onward. Now she stood at the altar rail, aware, yet incapable of doing anything to prevent events from taking their course. She thought she spied a worried look on the face of the man before her, whom she had identified vaguely as a cleric.

As well she might have done, for the Reverend Inkberrow was extremely disturbed. Not that he was in any way surprised by the appearance in his church of the bridal couple and their family. He had read the banns these past Sundays, and had been expecting this event. What concerned him was the suddenness of the final arrangements for the wedding—he had had to postpone a local christening to accommodate it—and the apparent illness of the bride.

All well and good, he thought, for the Henlows to protest that the girl had insisted on it, being afraid that her indisposition might, like her father's before her, have disastrous results. But she did not look as if she was capable of insisting on anything. She looked as if she ought to be tucked up in her bed. The parson appreciated that she might well wish to secure her prospective husband's future by the marriage, which would, he knew, put Sir Jeremy in possession of his rightful inheritance. For all the village knew of the extraordinary nature of Sir Clement's will. It seemed, however, rather cruel to drag the child out in her present state.

'I could very well have performed the ceremony at Dunhythe, sir, if only you had informed me of the circumstances,' he had told the Major.

But Henlow had shaken his head. His intention was to make everything appear normal and above board. There must be nothing furtive about the marriage. That might indicate that there was something to hide.

'I fear it would not have answered. My niece, foolhardy though it appears, was set on a proper wedding. We could not bring ourselves to deny it to her.'

So Reverend Inkberrow had perforce to agree. But, as he began the initial address of the marriage service to the congregation, he began again to have doubts. Miss Clementina Hythe appeared to know what was required of her, for she had journeyed quiescently up the aisle, albeit slowly, on Major

Henlow's arm. But he had been obliged to grip her hand tightly to prevent her from falling, and she leaned heavily on the support of Miss Margery Plumstead, who remained unusually at her side at the altar. Yet she was evidently relaxed. Too relaxed, perhaps, for a bride. Too pale, the green eyes upon him with almost—yes, a vacant look in them. Inwardly sighing, the parson concentrated upon his role.

'If anyone here present knows of any just cause or impediment——'

'Hold!'

The shout came from the back of the church. Startled, the cleric almost dropped his book. He looked up, and peered into the gloom at the other end of the nave.

Major Henlow jumped angrily to his feet. His son leapt up, and strode into the aisle.

'What do you mean by it, sir?' he demanded belligerently.

A man moved forward, down the aisle and into the light.

'The marriage cannot go forward,' announced the Earl of Sothern. 'There is an impediment.'

There was a brief pause, and the words hung on the air. Then pandemonium broke out as angry male voices rent the silence. The Reverend Inkberrow, too appalled to speak, glanced at the bride and saw her half swooning against the governess. Whether in shock or relief he could not tell. Pulling himself together, he moved into the fray.

'If you please, gentlemen,' he said quietly, and was surprised to find that everyone stopped talking. Gratified, he turned to the newcomer and discovered the real reason for the sudden hush. The intruder had produced a pistol, and was levelling it at Ellis Henlow's waistcoat. The cleric saw now that he was flanked on either side by two other men, similarly armed.

'Sir!' he sputtered. 'In God's house? This is an outrage!'

Sothern bowed in his direction. 'I make you my apologies, my good sir. I believe we may dispense with the weapons now that we have your attention.'

'What is the meaning of this?' demanded Mr Inkberrow, not in the least mollified to see the pistols disappearing into the pockets of all three gentlemen.

'I have said, sir, that the marriage cannot go forward.'

'And who might you be who dare to say so?'

'I am James, Lord Sothern, entirely at your service,' bowed Jake. A sharp hissing breath and the click of teeth told him that his name had made an impression on the Henlows, at least. The young man Ellis had apparently not recognised him from Lady Waldemar's rout. Though his pistol might have something to do with that, he thought, grimly smiling, for Ellis Henlow's eyes had been riveted on his weapon.

He motioned his two friends forward. 'Permit me to present Sir Harry Blaine and the Honourable Theodore Farleigh.'

Mr Inkberrow was not visibly moved. 'I shall not say that I am happy to make your acquaintance, my lord. You will please to inform me how you have the audacity to interrupt a holy ceremony.'

'With pleasure. Miss Hythe cannot espouse this gentleman, sir, for she has a prior commitment.' He tapped his own chest. 'To me.'

'What?' gasped the cleric.

'It is a damned lie!' shouted Major Henlow. 'Why, Mr Inkberrow here has read the banns these three weeks in this very church. For the marriage of Miss Hythe to Sir Jeremy.'

The parson nodded. 'That is very true. I am afraid your claim cannot be, my lord.'

'Indeed? Then let us put it to the test.' Jake moved forward, and at last saw Clementina. He drew a shocked breath. 'My God, what have you done to her?'

In two strides he was level with her and had seized her by the shoulders. *'Clementina!'*

She sagged in his grasp, but a whisper reached him. 'Jake. Thank God!'

Next moment she was in his arms, and his lips had claimed hers.

His plan had included the kiss, but not quite like this. He had meant to convey all the romance anyone could desire, but he had intended to whisper to her beforehand to feign enjoyment of his caress.

But there was no need of such pretence. That one glance at her wan face, and something had welled up inside him. A passion so strong that he had swept her into his arms without conscious thought, and his kiss contained everything that had caused him so to do.

In her drugged state Clementina knew only what she wanted, not what rational thought might prevent. Though her grasp was feeble, her arms snaked up around his neck and her lips responded hungrily to the intensity of his passion.

None of those watching, if they could think at all, could doubt of a prior attachment existing between the pair. Certainly Mr Inkberrow, though he flushed with embarrassment, could not find any logical argument to confound the Earl's assertions. Indeed, his own earlier doubts now seemed to burgeon more strongly.

He did not see the mask of cold fury worn by Ellis Henlow. Nor the ludicrous dismay on the faces of Ellis's parents, while Margery Plumstead looked on in fond complaisance, and the Earl's friends grinned their appreciation. But the bewilderment on the gaunt features of Sir Jeremy Hythe moved him to put an end to this scene.

'Lord Sothern, I beg of you!' he urged, in a tone of strong censure.

If Jake heard him he paid no heed. But, his kiss coming to a natural conclusion, he held Clementina cradled against his chest, and turned to glance directly at his two friends.

'I believe we can dispense with the company of the Henlows,' he said significantly.

'How right you are!' exclaimed Farleigh and, bowing to the major, he patted his pocket suggestively. Major Henlow began to protest, but, as Theo reached a hand into his pocket, he thought better of it, and left the church with rapid steps, defeated.

Sir Harry Blaine was more direct. 'Out!' he snapped, producing his pistol and waving it at Ellis.

Young Mr Henlow stood his ground and turned to throw a menacing glare on Lord Sothern. 'Be sure you will regret this, my lord.'

Prodded by Blaine's pistol, however, he retreated in some disorder.

Farleigh bowed to Mrs Henlow. 'If you please, ma'am. There is a wedding to be performed here, and you are not invited.'

Mrs Henlow started. 'You mean *he* is going to——? Oh, no!'

'Oh, yes,' Jake said firmly, and turned to the parson as his friends caused the protesting Mrs Henlow to vacate the church.

'Sir, I desire that you will marry us. Here is the special licence.' He held out the vital piece of paper that Theo Farleigh had brought back from London with him in the nick of time.

'Sir, I will do no such thing!' snapped the Reverend Inkberrow, outraged. 'You have violated the sanctity of my church, my lord, and nothing will induce me to perform the ceremony.'

Jake sighed. 'Miss Plumstead, take care of Clementina for me, if you please.'

He placed Clementina tenderly in one of the front pews, and left her to Margery's ministrations. Then he went up to where Jeremy still stood, gaping in utter confusion. Jake took him by the arm.

'Jeremy, you remember me?' The youth nodded. 'We talked this morning.'

'Y-yes. At—at the Bear.'

'That is correct. Well done. Do you remember signing this?'

'S-signed it,' Jeremy corroborated, looking at his own laboriously written signature at the bottom of the paper Sothern was holding out.

'And what does it say? Do you remember?'

Jeremy frowned. 'It s-says p-permission to m-marry C-Clemmy,' he got out.

'Who has permission?' asked Jake, and as the boy looked blank, repeated. 'Who may marry Clemmy, Jeremy?'

The youth shook a puzzled head. 'Y-you. N-not me. Y-you.'

'My lord, I protest!' the cleric burst out. 'You have deliberately worked upon the imperfections of this poor lad to serve your own ends. You know as well as I that his permission means nothing.'

'On the contrary,' Jake rejoined calmly. 'He is Clementina's legal guardian.'

'I know that, my lord. But it is nothing to the purpose. Why, he was ready not many minutes ago to espouse her himself. He is confused, poor boy, and no wonder!'

'My good sir,' Jake said, low-toned. 'I beg you to walk a little aside with me. I will tell you the whole, and perhaps that will induce you to change your mind.'

When the parson had heard the full story of the plot hatched by the Henlows he was so much appalled that he could only stare at the Earl for several moments.

'But—but this is fantastic! Are you certain of this?'

'Quite certain. Now will you marry us? It is the only means by which I can be sure to keep Clementina safe from their schemes.'

It took all the eloquence of which Lord Sothern was capable, together with the combined exhortations of his friends, but the parson was brought round in the end, and, with Sir Harry and Theo Farleigh as witnesses, the ceremony was at last performed.

It was a strange bridal for an Earl, with none of the expected silks richly embroidered in silver and stones. Only the bride, though simply dressed, was in remotely suitable clothes. The governess had graced the occasion with her best purple silk, an old-fashioned affair that added no glamour to the scene. Although Mr Farleigh had been charged with obtaining a change of gear for each of his friends, this consisted merely of linen and nightwear. So the groom and his supporters were most improperly clad in buckskins and topboots, with frock-coats over all, though mercifully their voluminous, caped greatcoats and beaver hats had been laid aside.

No one thought to ask Clementina, still under the influence of the drug, whether she was willing to marry Jake. But she made all her responses in a dreamy voice and with a smile playing about her lips. Afterwards Lord Sothern carried her outside and into the waiting chaise.

It was only when she awoke the next morning, in a strange bed in a strange room, that she regained the full possession of her senses. Turning as she began to wake, she opened her eyes.

With a small shriek she leapt from the bed and stood rigid, her horrified green gaze riveted on Jake's features, having discovered him sleeping peacefully on her pillow.

As Clementina stared, frozen in shock, Jake's eyes flickered open. He yawned, stretched, and became aware of the horrified gaze regarding him. Lazily, he smiled.

'Good morning, wife.'

Unable to take in the significance of this, Clementina found her voice.

'What,' she croaked feebly, 'are you doing there?'

His eyebrow lifted. 'Sleeping.'

'In *my* bed?'

'*Our* bed,' he corrected.

Clementina's lips opened and shut once or twice before she could get the words out.

'Have you—have you been there *all night*?' she managed in a faint voice.

'Most of it,' he responded, his eyes twinkling.

Weakly, Clementina fell back against the dresser behind her.

'I am ruined!' she uttered, her tone blank.

A laugh escaped Jake. 'It's all right, you goose. We are married.'

'*What?*'

'We are married,' he repeated calmly, raising himself in the bed to a sitting position and leaning back at his ease.

Clementina stared. She was shivering in her thin chemise, but whether from cold or the natural agitation of her shocked nerves even she could not tell. What he had said seemed impossible.

'I don't believe you!' she shot at him. 'You only say that to make me think all is well.'

His eyebrow was raised again. 'Would I lie to you?'

'*Yes,*' she said staunchly.

'Well, I would not. I promise you, we were married yesterday. Don't you remember?'

Clementina shook her head dumbly.

Jake sighed. 'Faith, that does not altogether surprise me. We were married by special licence yesterday,' he explained patiently, 'by the Reverend Inkberrow, in St Mark's Church at Dunhythe.'

Bewildered, Clementina uttered, 'Then—then why don't I recall it? Surely I would remember being married?'

'You were still half drugged, my child,' Jake said gently. 'Don't fret. I dare say it will all come back to you.'

'Don't fret? Don't *fret*?' Her voice rose. 'You sit there, in my room, in my *bed*, calmly informing me that I went through a marriage ceremony which I am quite unable to remember anything about, and you say *don't fret*!'

'Clementina, listen to me!'

He made to rise from the bed, and she backed away.

'Stay there! Don't come near me!'

Jake threw up his hand in a gesture of peace. 'I'm only going to get the marriage certificate.'

Still trembling, Clementina watched him get out
of the bed, blushing at the sight of his nightshirt.
He crossed to his frock-coat, which was placed with
his other clothes over the back of a chair. From it
he produced a folded paper which he opened and
held out, crossing the room towards her.

'Keep your distance!' Clementina warned him,
and her fingers twitched the thing at arm's length
from his outstretched hand. She read it, blinked
rapidly, and read it again.

'Now do you believe me?' Jake asked.

She did not look at him, but leaned back weakly
against the dresser. Her hand reached behind her
to place the paper carefully on top of it, as her
frowning gaze stared into the middle distance. A
memory stirred.

'The altar... I was at the altar. But it was—it
was *Jeremy*.'

Jake's voice came softly, not to interrupt her
grasp of the picture. 'It *was* Jeremy. But I came in
time, you see. I stopped it.'

Her eyes turned to his, but it was evident that
the images still filled her mind as she pieced them
together.

'You had pistols...there was an argument...
Margery had to hold me up, for I could not stand.
Then—then *you*... Oh, dear Lord! I thought it was
a dream. I thought the whole thing a nightmare
dream. But it happened! It really happened.'

She covered her eyes with her hands, shuddering
uncontrollably as the memories crowded in. Then
she felt Jake's touch. Blind panic took her. Her eyes

flew open and she thrust him away, leaping on to the bed and out the other side.

'You tricked me!' she threw at him across the bed. 'You knew I was half insensible and you took advantage of it.'

'It wasn't like that at all,' Jake said. 'It was un-fortunate, but——'

'Unfortunate!'

'Yes, unfortunate. There was no time to wait for you to recover. The matter was urgent.'

'Then it is even more urgent to end it,' Clementina cried desperately, a trapped sensation overcoming all reason.

'What is that supposed to mean?' Jake rapped out.

'What is done can be undone. At once. I shall say how you tricked me, and the marriage will be annulled.'

'Over my dead body!'

'If necessary, yes!'

There was a sudden silence. Jake's dark eyes met and held hers.

'Do you dislike it as much as that?' he asked quietly.

Clementina did not answer this. 'You tricked me,' she said again, defensive. 'You knew I would never have married you otherwise. You *knew*.'

Jake stiffened. 'You made no protest.'

'Of course I made no protest. I was patently in-capable of making any protest.'

'Does that apply to last night?'

Speech was wiped from her lips. In ludicrous dismay she stared at him. Then at the bed between them. Then at him again.

'You mean you—I——?' She could not continue.

Jake studied her in a considering way. 'You'll be telling me you don't remember that either, I suppose.'

Her lip began to tremble. God help her, but she did not remember!

'As I recall,' Jake went on, 'there was a good deal worth remembering.'

'Oh, no!' Clementina whispered, and a tear crept over her lashes to steal down her cheek. She bit her lip and ran agitated fingers through her hair.

Her white and worried features reminded Jake of the way she had looked when he had seen her at the altar the day before. Then another picture intruded. Of firelight flickering over her countenance where she sat by the hearth, the white shoulder and the teasing little mound of one pert breast peeping from the folds of her dressing-gown. Now here she was, still all tousled from sleep. And all his! Fire engulfed him.

Having no idea how desirable she looked, Clementina remained unaware that Jake's dark eyes raked her with a burning glance.

'Clementina!' burst from him suddenly. 'Oh, God, Clementina!'

In a moment he was around the bed and had seized her in a powerful grip. His hot gaze devoured her, and she, powerless to resist, melted under the onslaught of his passion.

Their lips met in a clinging, smouldering kiss. Lambent flame ran over Clementina's body, and her knees buckled under her. Her brain dizzy, she felt herself lifted. Then the softness of the bed was under her, the hard body of her husband pressing her down. She was beyond any thought, beyond any care. Sensation took her over and she gave herself up to Jake's expert lovemaking.

Yet even in the throes of her own passion she was aware of the tenderness, the gentleness and care with which he took her. There was pain, but under his skilful manipulation it became exquisite pleasure. Clementina had never imagined the existence of such ecstasy.

Afterwards, blissful, she lay cradled in his arms, willing this moment to go on forever. Until Jake, leaning to murmur in her ear, shattered it into fragments.

'I lied, Clementina. That was the first time.'

Instantly Clementina's hot temper flared. Wrenching herself out of his hold, she sat up and turned on him, a raging fury, small fists pummelling at his chest.

'You wicked, deceitful wretch! How could you? How *could* you? I'll never forgive you. Never, *never*!'

'Stop it, you little devil!' laughingly protested his lordship, catching at her wrists and drawing out of the way.

'You beast! You brute!' she panted, writhing to free herself. 'I'll make you sorry you ever dared to do this!'

'If you drive me into ill-humour, my girl,' Jake threatened, holding her off, 'it is you who will be sorry.'

But as he was still grinning Clementina was spurred to even greater fury. Swivelling on the bed, she kicked at him.

'Sweet Heaven! You wildcat!' he uttered, endeavouring to maintain his hold on her wrists, and striving to anchor her flailing legs with his own.

'I hate you! I hate you!' Clementina flung at him, kicking wildly.

Getting a purchase on the bed, Jake managed to swing himself up and over so that he straddled her. His body held hers down so that her flailing legs found no target, and he pushed her arms back and pinned them to the pillows.

'Now, will you stop?' he demanded of the up-turned, flushed face as she threshed uselessly beneath him.

For answer, Clementina turned her head and sank sharp, white teeth deeply into his hand.

'Ye Gods!' yelled Jake, and wrenched his hand back, releasing her wrist.

Quick as a flash Clementina was up, butting her head into his chest. His breath caught momentarily. Letting go of her other wrist, he toppled backwards and she wriggled free.

Next moment she was off the bed and heading for the door, only to be brought up short by the sudden realisation that she was stark naked. She turned and looked wildly round for her clothing, her hands desperately shifting in an effort to cover her nudity.

Jake knelt cursing on the bed as he fought for breath, his dark eyes alight with anger.

'By—my faith!' he swore between gulps of air. 'If I . . . don't take a . . . stick to you, you may count yourself . . . fortunate . . . my lady Sothern.'

'Don't call me by that name!' Clementina flung at him. 'Why did you lie to me?'

Jake drew a shuddering sigh as his breathing eased, and sank back on his heels. His anger drained away. Searching in the mussed bedclothes, he located Clementina's chemise and threw it to her.

'Here—put this on.' Then, at her suspicious look as she caught it, 'Don't worry. I'm not going to . . . chase you round the room.'

Clementina disappeared inside the chemise and, as her head came out of it, she saw that Jake was off the bed and already tugging on his discarded breeches.

'Where are my other clothes?' she asked, as she watched him dress. 'And you haven't answered my question. Why did you lie?'

Jake took time over his answer. He concentrated on tying his ruined neck-cloth, and did not look at her.

'I didn't want you to have any grounds for an annulment. That is all.' He crossed to the bed and tugged on the bell-rope. 'I gave your gown to a maid last night. I trust it will be freshly pressed by now. You will need water, too.'

'Wait!' Clementina said, stopping him as he headed for the door. 'You need not go. I—I suppose you want also to wash. And that neck-cloth looks none too fresh.'

'I have linen in my room next door,' he replied shortly.

'Then you did not need to sleep here at all!' she exclaimed indignantly. 'It was all done on purpose.'

He shrugged. 'You will do me the justice to own that I at least waited for you to be in your senses.'

Tears pricked at Clementina's eyelids. She felt used. Turning from him, she said in gruff tones, 'I can't think why you went to so much trouble.'

'I have told you. I married you to protect you from your relatives. Small point in so doing, if you were going to seek an annulment at the first opportunity.'

There was a knock at the door, and he went to open it.

'One moment!' Clementina called, turning back to him.

He hesitated, his fingers on the door handle. 'Yes?'

'What now? I mean, where are we going?'

'Home. Where else?'

Clementina bit her lip. 'Home? You mean your house in London?'

'*Our* house. There are some privileges attached to being my wife,' Jake remarked, a faint note of mockery in his tone.

She looked down, her hands absently smoothing the chemise against her slim body.

'Could we——?' she began hesitantly. 'Do you— do you think we might visit your grandmother first? She—she really ought to know what has transpired.'

'As you wish,' he said, apparently indifferent. 'Anything else?'

'No. No, that is all.' She looked up, and her gaze was bleak. 'Thank you.'

Jake frowned slightly and hesitated, as if he would say something more. But Clementina turned away towards the mirror over the dresser. Compressing his lips, he opened the door. A maid stood outside. Nodding at her to enter, he left the room.

CHAPTER NINE

THE journey to London was accomplished by hired chaise. Jake had taken the precaution of leaving Lodeton the previous day and taking his bride some part of the way on the road to London before putting up at one of the better coaching inns. Sir Harry Blaine had driven Jake's phaeton back to London, as it had been necessary to hire the chaise to carry Clementina in her semi-drugged condition.

But the journey was not a happy one. The atmosphere was strained and uncomfortable, with both passengers alone with their thoughts.

The Earl had not known that he could be so bitterly hurt by Clementina's whole-hearted rejection. After they had made love with such physical abandon as he had never met with in a girl so young and innocent he had naturally assumed that the ease of intimacy would spill over into their day-to-day relationship. But his new wife—his *wife*! Oh, the thrill of possession in that word!—was not to be so easily conquered, it seemed.

There must be a way to win her. To *woo* her, damn it to hell! Had he not shown his passion? What must he do, for the love of heaven?

A small voice reminded him of those words of hers that night. How long ago it seemed now! Yet it was but a few days. 'Far too old'. Was that the truth? Something heavy seemed to weigh on his heart. For the first time in his life he cast about in his mind for ways in which to make himself acceptable to a woman.

As for Clementina, her thoughts were even less happy. She felt cheated. She was, too, furious with herself. How could she have been so lost to all sense of decency? What must he think of her? Well, it was obvious what he thought of her. She had sworn never to swell the ranks of his conquests. And what had happened? At the first onslaught she had crumbled like any of his numerous flames, and fallen deep into the abyss of her own secret desires. She could no longer conceal from herself the depths of her passion for this man. And like any blind, fanciful miss she had succumbed to his wiles, thinking that his caresses meant more than the natural animal instinct of a confirmed rake. What a romantic idiot!

'Well, no more!' she muttered under her breath. 'Never again.'

Sothern's voice startled her. 'I beg your pardon!'

'Nothing,' she said hastily, taking a grip on her trembling underlip, and turning her eyes firmly to gaze out of the plate-glass window at the post-boy's back.

'What is the matter?' he persisted.

'Nothing at all,' she repeated, not looking at him.

There was a pause. Then Jake cleared his throat. 'I realise there has been no time to think of the future, but we may as well make some plans.'

Clementina turned her head, suspicion in the green eyes. 'What plans?'

'Well, you are, though you do not yet realise it, mistress of a fairly extensive establishment.'

'Indeed?' There was no vestige of interest in her tone.

'Indeed.' His own voice hardening involuntarily, Jake pressed on. 'There is my town house in Albemarle Street. It is not a family residence, so if you don't wish to live there it may readily be disposed of.'

'I cannot imagine why I should have anything to say in the matter,' Clementina said stiffly.

'I am trying to make it easy for you,' he maintained in an even stiffer tone.

'Pray, don't trouble, sir. For my part, you may continue precisely in the same way.'

'Don't be stupid!' Jake snapped, losing control. 'How can I possibly do so?'

Clementina was silent. There was nothing she wanted less than to discuss the details of this empty marriage. There was no anticipation, no pleasure for her in thinking of the life to come. She had rather not think of it. But to say so would only lead to further argument, and she was too tired, still too much dragged down by recent events. In a word, she was not herself.

The Earl took her silence for acquiescence, and began again to attempt to gain her co-operation.

'Of course, you may wish to make changes. I dare say there are insufficient servants in a bachelor establishment, for instance, to attend to your needs. Then I suppose we must entertain on a more substantial scale.'

He warmed to his task as the idea of a married life with Clementina took hold of his imagination.

'We will return to Berkshire, naturally, once the season draws to a close. You will like the estates, I am persuaded. The original part of the house is old. Jacobean. But my father added to it in the prevailing Palladian mode during the era of Capability Brown. He did an excellent job on the landscaping, too. You may easily pursue there the activities you enjoy. But, if you prefer, we can always go to one of the watering-places for the summer months. Brighthelmstone has become quite the rage since the Prince took to going there. Or, if you are set against the fashionable life, there is always the outmoded Wells.'

He paused as she turned at last to regard him with a cynical eye.

'If the recitation of all these dubious delights in store is supposed to reconcile me to my lot, my lord, let me tell you that it has failed in its object. I am not interested.'

'Then you had better cultivate an interest,' Jake told her curtly. 'For better or worse we are married. You may as well make the best of it.'

'How can I,' she cried, a catch in her voice, 'when for me there is only the *worse*?'

It was as if she had struck him. He drew back, away from her, leaning into his own corner.

Clementina turned her head and gazed steadfastly from the window, her eyes bright with unshed tears.

Not one word more was exchanged for the remainder of the journey. A journey which began to seem interminable, the atmosphere between the bridal pair being what it was. Each would have found it hard to imagine a less propitious beginning to a marriage.

It was around four in the afternoon by the time the chaise finally drew up at Lady Staplegrove's town house, and Clementina for one was exhausted. What with the rigours of the past two days, and the tension between herself and this man she must now call husband, she felt as if her body had been beaten with cudgels and her brain mashed with a giant fork.

Lady Staplegrove was at home, clad in her customary silken undress for comfort, sitting as was her wont in the pink parlour, a volume of Mrs Parsons' Gothic romance *The Castle of Wolfenbach* open upon her knee. She looked up as the door opened. When she saw Clementina hovering uncertainly on the threshold she laid her book aside and jumped up, her face wreathed in smiles.

'My dear, dear child! Thank heaven! I have been worried to death.'

She enfolded Clementina in a warm embrace, and drew her into the room. 'There, my dear, come in.'

She took in how drawn the girl looked then, the cream of the muslin wedding-gown she still wore emphasising her pallor. The dowager tutted anxiously.

'You look quite shattered. Some tea, that is what you want. Dorridge shall see to it on the instant.'

'Thank you, ma'am. That would be wonderful,' Clementina said, sitting on the sofa towards which the dowager was pushing her. She retained her clasp on the old lady's hand.

'Dear ma'am, I am so happy to see you again. And there is so much to tell you. I am afraid you may not quite like it, however.'

'Oh, tush! What nonsense! Why should I not like it, pray? But don't tell me anything yet.'

She turned to cross busily towards the door, and noticed her grandson leaning negligently against the jamb. She bustled over with hands held out.

'Sothern, I declare you are a wizard! You found her. I am so pleased with you.'

Jake could not forebear a smile as he took her hands and kissed them. 'That makes a change.'

'Does it not?' laughed his grandmother. She peered closely at him. 'Dear me! You are looking a trifle fagged yourself, boy. I dare say you could do with some wine. Now where is that butler of mine?'

'I am here, my lady,' said Dorridge, appearing from the hallway. 'Wine for his lordship, and tea for Miss Hythe and yourself, my lady?'

'Excellent creature! You always know, don't you?'

Dorridge bowed, and refrained from mentioning that he knew simply because he had overheard her earlier remarks. As he withdrew her ladyship turned to beam upon the two.

'Well, gracious me! This is so exciting. I don't know if I am on my head or my heels!'

The Earl's eyebrow went up ironically. 'Loath as I am to add to these distressing symptoms, ma'am, we do have some news that really cannot wait.'

'Jake, don't,' Clementina begged. 'Not yet.' She covered her eyes with her hands for a moment.

Lady Staplegrove looked from one to the other expectantly. 'I scent a mystery. Well? Get on, one of you. Don't keep me in suspense.'

Jake looked at Clementina. 'Shall I, or will you?'

Clementina lowered her hands from her face and sat up straighter, bravely looking her ladyship in the eye.

'I am sorry, ma'am, if our news displeases you, but I promise you it was not my fault.'

'Quite true,' cut in his lordship. 'You see, Grandmama, Clementina is no longer Miss Hythe. Yesterday she became Lady Sothern.'

The dowager's jaw dropped visibly. Faintly, she uttered, 'Lord above!' Then a slow smile crept over her face and she was laughing.

'Oh, what a joke! What a wondrous twist of fate!' Almost waltzing up to Clementina, she seized her hands. 'My dear, my dear, I could not be more delighted. You will scarcely believe me, but only the other night at Lady Waldemar's the thought crossed my mind. But I supposed it could never be. Oh, Clementina, dearest child! You have made me so very happy!'

She was laughing and crying at once, sitting down by the bewildered girl to clasp her in her arms. Then she was up again, dancing over to embrace her grandson.

'Sothern, it is wonderful. How often have I wished for just such a thing! Now must you at last settle down to steady sobriety.'

With an effort Jake managed a smile. But Lady Staplegrove, always acutely aware of his moods, sensed at once that her elation was not shared.

'What is it?' she asked straitly. 'Is there some hitch?'

Jake shook his head. 'Not at all,' he said stiffly.

'Don't tell me! I can read you like a book. Something is wrong.' She turned to Clementina, who was sitting white-faced and stonily silent. 'My love, you are distressed!'

Clementina looked up at her, the green eyes swimming. 'It—it is not what you think, ma'am. Truly. The—the marriage is purely for—for convenience, that is all. Jake believed that by—by wedding me himself he might k-keep me safe from the m-machinations of my uncle and cousin. It— it is indeed chivalrous of him, and I s-suppose I ought to be grateful.' Her voice cracked. 'But I am *not*!'

Lady Staplegrove glanced from Clementina's woeful countenance to Jake's set features and drew her own swift conclusions. She came to the sofa, and taking Clementina's hand, patted it comfortingly.

'You are overwrought, dear child. There! We will talk no more of it for the present.'

At this opportune moment the door opened to admit Dorridge with a tray of refreshments, and Lucy the housemaid, bearing a large urn.

'Ah, see! Here is our tea,' said the dowager instantly. 'Just exactly what we are needing. Do you place it over here, Lucy, and I will pour. Dorridge, see to his lordship, if you please.'

As the servants busied themselves she whispered, 'Try to compose yourself, dearest girl. Later I shall send Sothern about his business and we may enjoy a comfortable cose.'

Insensibly reassured, Clementina swallowed on the rising tears and meekly sipped her tea, thankful for the moment to lay the burden of her heavy heart on other shoulders.

While the servants were in the room Lady Staplegrove maintained a monologue on the latest society gossip, and the light flow of idle talk seemed to soothe Clementina's lacerated nerves. But once Dorridge and the maid had left the room Lady Staplegrove turned to her grandson.

'Now, Sothern, give me a round tale, if you please. What has been happening these two days?'

While Jake gave her an unvarnished account of his activities, up to the point of the exchange of vows between himself and Clementina, his bride kept her gaze firmly on her teacup, and did not once glance in his direction. Though his eyes strayed frequently, his grandmother noted, to dwell a moment on the bent head with its crown of gold-red curls.

When he had finished the dowager sat for a while in thoughtful silence, her own gaze resting on Clementina.

'Yes,' she said at length, and gave a satisfied nod.

The bride glanced up at her, startled, and Lord Sothern's eyebrow rose.

'Is there some meaning behind that cryptic utterance, ma'am?'

'Don't get uppish with me, Sothern,' warned Lady Staplegrove. 'Instead of exercising your dubious wit, think on this. Do you imagine such ruthless men as the Henlows have proved to be may be silenced by this means?'

Jake shrugged. 'I should suppose not. But there is nothing they can do.'

His grandmother regarded him somewhat enigmatically. 'Then you are to be congratulated. And now be off with you!'

Sothern's brow darkened. 'Do you know, Grandmama, there are times when I regret my obligations as a relative.'

'So do I,' retorted the dowager. 'Heartily. Now go away, do. I wish to converse with my newly acquired granddaughter, and your presence is superfluous.'

The Earl gritted his teeth. 'I don't think my wife has any need of female instruction in her forthcoming role.'

'So I should suppose,' scoffed her ladyship. 'I am not going to attempt anything of that nature, I assure you. I don't doubt you are sufficiently equipped to accomplish such instruction quite adequately on your own.'

Clementina blushed scarlet and averted her face, while Jake, no less embarrassed, almost ground his teeth. Lady Staplegrove rose, and came to tuck a hand into her grandson's stiffened arm. She urged him towards the door.

'Dear boy,' she said, low-voiced, 'can you not see that the poor child is in desperate need of unburdening herself of her woes? I dare say there is a great deal more to be told than you are aware of yourself. I am sure you must be able to find something to do for an hour or so.'

So saying, she thrust him gently from the room and shut the door upon him. She waited a moment, her ear bent to the woodwork, until she heard his footsteps cross the hall and the front door open and shut behind him. Then she crossed back to the sofa and held out her hands.

'Come, my dear.'

Clementina looked up at her, puzzled. 'Why, ma'am, where are we going?'

'To your bedchamber. Don't you feel in need of rest?'

'Yes, indeed I do. But how do you mean, *my* bedchamber? Surely——?'

'My dear child, this is your home now.'

Clementina blinked at her. 'Here? But Jake said we must go to his house.'

'Don't let that worry you.' A mischievous twinkle entered the old lady's eye. 'I can handle Jake.'

'I still don't understand, ma'am,' Clementina said much later, as she sat up in bed sipping at a glass of hot milk.

Her eyes were red and swollen from crying, but the relief of being permitted to weep out her story was tremendous. Lady Staplegrove had sat and listened, interpolating only an encouraging word here and there, and proffering a fresh handkerchief when Clementina's proved inadequate to cope with the deluge of tears. Afterwards her ladyship had recommended her to bathe her swollen eyes with

Hungary water, and had sent for the milk, declaring her intention of leaving young Lady Sothern to sleep. But Clementina had detained her, still burningly curious.

'Why do you permit me to remain here, when you know that Sothern has every right to demand that I go with him to Albemarle Street?'

Lady Staplegrove sat down again on the bed. 'Let us say that I have every sympathy with your situation. You need a little time to...' she paused, eyeing the girl in a considering way '... to adjust perhaps?'

Clementina set down the empty glass. 'I don't know. I cannot think what I am to do. It is not—it is not that I dislike Jake, you understand.'

'Oh, yes, I understand that,' said the dowager, a smile flickering on her lips.

'Yes. Well, you see, he—he does not——' Clementina drew a steadying breath, and looked up at Lady Staplegrove with that direct gaze. 'He decided to marry me, you see. He did not ask. There was no courtship. No words of—of love. Oh, he desires me! That much is plain.'

A delicate colour entered her cheeks, and she could no longer meet Lady Staplegrove's twinkling eyes. Her fingers plucked restlessly at the sheet.

'It even crossed my mind that he might have married me for that reason. I mean, there was no other way he could ... I would not have ...'

'I take your meaning, child, never fear,' interpolated the dowager, with an amused laugh.

'Yes, well. Perhaps it is not so. Because, after all, he must know from past experience that he will soon weary of me, and then where would he be?'

'Where, indeed?'

'Unless perhaps his—his wishes might have clouded his judgement?' Clementina suggested.

She met the dowager's gaze as she spoke, and her ladyship thought she detected a wistful look in the green eyes.

'We do not know that his *wishes* enter into the matter at all,' commented Lady Staplegrove. 'Though any man who ties himself up in matrimony for a purely altruistic motive to someone he does not at all wish to marry must in my estimation be counted little better than a lunatic!'

Clementina let out an involuntary giggle. 'I don't believe he is quite that—yet.'

'But you suppose that marriage to you might conceivably make him so?'

'Oh, ma'am!' Clementina protested, gurgling again.

Lady Staplegrove leaned forward and kissed her cheek. 'How good to see you laugh! Now go to sleep, silly child. Men are the oddest creatures, you know. But the right woman may tame the wildest of them.'

Upon which cryptic utterance, she tucked the bedclothes about Clementina and kissed her again. Then, turning down the oil-lamp on the bedside-table so that only a warm glow filled the room, and drawing the curtains on the bed a little way to shield the sleeper from the light, she tiptoed quietly from the room.

Thus it was that when Lord Sothern came to fetch his bride home he found only his grandmother—in implacable mood.

'This is absurd, Grandmama!' he protested. 'As if Clementina was afraid of me!'

'Nothing of the sort,' rejoined her ladyship. 'She is quite exhausted, and I can see no virtue in dragging her up out of her bed at this time of night.'

'It is barely nine o'clock,' Jake said drily.

'Is it? Dear me! I had thought it much later, so much passion as has been expended this day.'

Jake controlled his temper with difficulty. 'Understand me, ma'am. I will not permit you, or anyone, to prevent my taking my wife to her rightful home.'

Lady Staplegrove raised her brows. 'Well, really, Sothern! I had not thought you to be guilty of cruelty.'

'I have no intention of being cruel. I merely wish——'

'If you cannot see that it would be nothing short of cruel to snatch that poor child from her much-needed rest, then I must suppose you to be so. She is well-nigh exhausted, poor little soul!'

The Earl eyed her in a frustrated way. 'Very well. But I warn you that I mean to fetch her home first thing in the morning.'

His grandmother pursed her lips, and made a business of arranging her skirts about the pink brocade sofa. 'You know, I have been thinking about that, and I believe it will be best for her to remain with me for the present.'

'What?'

She held up a finger to silence him. 'Now just think for one minute, Sothern, if you please. This marriage of yours has been conducted in an extremely havey-cavey fashion. You must take care if you don't wish it to give rise to unseemly gossip.'

'If you imagine that I give tuppence,' said his lordship sneeringly, 'for the mouthings of a parcel of busybodies, you very much mistake the matter.'

'I dare say you don't. You might give something for the harm it could do to your wife, however.'

Silenced, Sothern glared at her. He took a hasty turn about the room, and returned to stand before her.

'It can't be helped. The thing is done now, and the sooner we face the consequences, the better.'

'The better for whom?' scoffingly demanded his grandmother. 'Don't be such a ninny, Sothern! Tell me this. What have you said to Blaine and Farleigh on the matter?'

'They are sworn to secrecy, of course.'

'Excellent. Now here is what I suggest. I have set it about already that my young friend, Miss Hythe, is indisposed. We shall have her reappear in society, and——'

'As Miss Hythe?' interrupted Sothern incredulously. 'She's my *wife*!'

Lady Staplegrove stamped her foot. 'Don't interrupt me, boy! She will reappear, I say, as *Miss Hythe*. You will dangle after her. I will let drop broad hints about my expectations of a whirlwind romance.'

'If this is leading up to a second marriage ceremony, you may believe that nothing will induce

me to lend myself to any such farce,' said Jake
snappily.

'Oh, for goodness' sake!' cried his grandmother,
exasperated. 'Do you take me for a nincompoop?
I wish you will mend your temper and attend to
what I am saying.'

She paused, but Jake did not venture upon another retort, though his dark eyes glowered
resentfully.

'After a decent interval,' she went on, 'you and
Clementina will depart from London for whatever
destination you choose, leaving behind a notice of
your marriage in the Gazette, and giving out that
you have gone on your honeymoon. Now what have
you to say?'

Lord Sothern compressed his lips. Nothing could
have exceeded his dislike of the whole enterprise
but, as he was quite unable to find a single reasonable objection to put forward, he was left without
a word to say.

'Have you put this fantastic scheme to
Clementina?' he asked instead.

'Not yet,' Lady Staplegrove admitted.

'Then I shall reserve my decision until I have discussed the matter with her tomorrow.'

'Certainly, if she is willing to receive you.'

'She had better be!' Jake said curtly.

The dowager raised her brows. 'If you mean to
approach her in that deplorable spirit I can vouch
for it that she will not be willing.'

'No, because you have worked upon her so that
she hates me!'

'If she does,' responded Lady Staplegrove repressively, 'it is not for anything I have done.'

The Earl flung away from her to the fire, and stood drumming his fingers on the mantelpiece. Then he turned, and his grandmother saw that he was very pale, his jaw set.

'I should not have said that, Grandmama. I beg your pardon.'

'Never mind it,' she said, and smiled. 'For my part, if it comforts you, I do not believe for a moment that Clementina hates you.'

Light flickered briefly in the dark eyes, and died again, leaving them sombre.

'Nevertheless, she regrets the marriage. You need not pretend that she did not ask sanctuary of you. She does not wish to come back with me to Albemarle Street. That is it, is it not? You have devised this elaborate plot only to keep her safe from me for as long as possible. As though I had been an ogre!' he said bitterly.

Lady Staplegrove hid a smile. She rose and came up to him to pat his cheek. 'Go home, Jake. Or go and cool your passions elsewhere.'

The Earl cast his eyes to heaven. 'Faith, you are the most infuriating person I know, Grandmama! Very well. Have it your own way. But don't think I mean to dance attendance on a recalcitrant bride, for I have better things to do with my time!'

He left her on the words, and his grandmother heard the front door slam behind him. She walked calmly to the bell-pull and gave it a tug.

'Dorridge,' she said, when the butler entered, 'bring me a glass of that port your master laid down before he died.'

'The '83, my lady?' the butler queried, and, though both surprised and curious, he spoke as if quite unmoved.

But the dowager knew better. 'You think I have run mad, eh? No, no. My dear husband warned me that I should on no account touch the stuff except when the occasion demanded so great an honour.'

Dorridge bowed. 'As you say, my lady.'

'So bring it, Dorridge.' She shot him a look brimful of mischief. 'I have something momentous to celebrate!'

While her ladyship was enjoying her private joke her grandson was striding through the streets towards his own home, his foul mood worsening with every step.

He had had ample time in which to regret everything he had said that day, everything he had done. Particularly his manner of disclosing to Clementina the news that she was now Lady Sothern. For he had known the night before how unlikely it was that she would recall it. Indeed, he had not meant to force his presence on her at all. But before retiring for the night he had crept quietly into the room in which the chambermaid had tucked her up in bed on their arrival at the inn. She had looked so young and helpless, so innocently vulnerable, her pale face on the pillow hauntingly beautiful, that he had found it impossible to leave her.

Now it appeared as if all understanding between them was at an end. And here was his grandmother, making it impossible for him even to attempt to bridge the gulf. He was positive that Clementina had thrown herself upon Lady Staplegrove's mercy. Plainly she had no wish for him to repeat this morning's episode. God in heaven, she had made her views on their marriage plain enough!

He had found time to bathe and change, had dressed with extra care in a suit of blue and grey that he knew looked well on him. All the time with his mind on what he would say to her, how he would conduct himself. He would begin again, try a different tack. But now he could not even see her, let alone woo her!

Fighting down his disappointment, Jake lashed resentment into a flame. After all, he had freely given to Clementina what many another woman would jump at. He could not count the caps that had been set at him through the years by hopeful young débutantes, the traps he had skirted laid by many a matchmaking mama. But not Miss Hythe! Oh, no. She had rather wed a half-wit and live in the wilds of Norfolk. The Earl of Sothern, with his town house, his Berkshire estates, and a secure place in the fashionable world, she scorned with all the contempt of a princess of the blood royal! An annulment, indeed! How dared she? And immediately after he had made the most exquisite love to her, too!

He stopped dead suddenly. Very well. If my lady Sothern had no use for his caresses, there were others who did. He turned and headed off in a different direction, making for Half Moon Street.

Whether Lady Matilda Ingleby would be at home was another matter. If so, she was certain to be alone, for Mr Ingleby, as Jake knew, spent every evening at his club, rolling home always in the small hours somewhat the worse for drink. If Maud was out the porter would tell him where she had gone. Likely enough, any party she graced he would also have an invitation to attend.

In fact, Lady Matilda had not gone out that evening. She greeted him in her boudoir, her form enveloped in the cloud of gauze that constituted her négligé. She lounged seductively on a chaise-longue. She had for him a delighted smile and a roguish look as she complained of his two-day absence from town.

'And never a word of your whereabouts to poor little me,' she said in her melodious voice. 'Not a hint as to how long you might be away.'

'I didn't know myself,' Jake said shortly, and his kiss was perfunctory. He had become abruptly aware of a feeling of distaste as her full lips pressed against his.

Maud reached up to cup his face between her hands. Her dark, lustrous eyes gave him a languorous look.

'I've missed you so much.'

As she drew his head down and leaned up to him, her eyes closing, Jake was assailed by an image of Clementina's piquant features. He shut his eyes in an effort to banish it, and felt again the sensual probing of Maud's mouth. She was rising to sit up, pulling him close, her ample, voluptuous form pressing against him.

Automatically he responded, but there was no answering fire in his loins. Why had he never realised how stout Maud was growing? he wondered. And how in Hades could he get out of here?

Lady Matilda, apparently sensing his lack of interest, drew back and looked at him, a slight frown creasing her brow.

'What is it, dearest?'

Jake released himself from her embrace, rose from the chaise-longue, and moved away from her to stand before the fire. 'I am a trifle fagged, that is all.'

Maud gave rather an artificial laugh. 'Oh, well! If you are too tired to pleasure me...' She shrugged her shoulders in a gesture of apparent unconcern.

'It is not that.'

'No? Then what?'

Lady Matilda's tone was becoming brittle. She was, in fact, furious with him, but she was far too clever to show it. The rumours had reached her ears about the young girl seen in the park with him the other day, as had the subsequent appearance of Miss Hythe under Lady Staplegrove's escort, which silenced them. But she was by no means satisfied of Sothern's disinterest. His unaccountable absence from town, coinciding with the sudden indisposition of this fresh young débutante had filled her with misgiving. That the two events were unconnected she could not believe.

A demon of jealousy slept uneasily in her bosom. Jake was her conquest, and she could by no means tolerate his defection to another. Especially one with the obvious advantages of youth. Experience, however, had warned her to tread warily. One did not force an issue with a man of Sothern's stamp. Gently, gently one had to go to work!

So Lady Maud curbed her natural irritation and let only the slightest of feminine wiles appear in the form of a sultry reproach.

'Dearest, this is not how you are wont to greet me.'

Sothern kicked at the smouldering logs in the grate. Then he sighed, and turned to give his mistress a deprecating smile.

'Forgive me, my dear. I am out of temper.'

'That much I had deduced for myself,' Maud said tartly. Then she laughed. 'But don't let us quarrel.'

She rose languidly, crossed to him, and slid her arms around his neck. 'Come, my heart. Relax, and I will mend all for you.'

Her lustrous eyes beckoned him, and her heady perfume filled his nostrils. For a moment he gave himself up to the sensations she produced with her wandering hands. Then came her voluptuous kiss again, and the memories rose once more to taunt him with the sweet tenderness of Clementina's lips, the joys of her slim form, the magic of her precious innocence.

Unable to control himself, he pulled his mouth free and thrust Maud rudely from him.

'I cannot, I cannot,' he muttered, anguished.

After Clementina's freshness he could not endure the jaded intensity of this woman's overpowering lust. It was as if his eyes were suddenly opened to her true nature. Maud's insatiability had always intrigued him, had spurred him to greater heights in his efforts to satisfy her. Now it disgusted him, and he wondered how he had borne it for so long.

Maud's control slipped rapidly.

'How dare you?' she demanded in a low, vibrant voice. 'How dare you treat me so?'

Aware that his disgracefully discourteous action called for apology, Jake was yet unable to utter the words.

'I told you,' he said, his jaw set. 'I am tired. I am not in the mood.'

'When a man claims to be tired,' replied Lady Matilda, her voice trembling with anger, 'it usually means that he has taken his toll of a rival.' She paused, eyeing him with acute suspicion. 'Well? Am I right?'

'There is no rival,' Jake snapped. Ye Gods! Was he to place Clementina in that category? No, by God, he would not!

'No?' Maud was silky suddenly, her native wariness winning over her baser self, urging her to tread with care. 'Then *something*, if not *someone*, has denuded you of your natural desires.'

His eyebrow lifted. 'What utter nonsense you talk! I am merely tired. Tired and preoccupied. And I should not have come here.'

'That much is evident,' she observed sharply. Then she managed a smile. 'Go, then. I shall expect you when you are less "preoccupied".'

Jake shifted, ill at ease. 'I can't tell when that may be.'

'It does not matter. I can wait.' As he hesitated she suddenly turned the subject. 'I trust your grandmother's young friend is recovering from her indisposition?'

Jake's head jerked round. 'What?'

'Miss—Hythe, is it not?' said Maud, falsely sweet. 'She is well?'

A dark flush overspread Sothern's features, but he answered with tolerable composure.

'She is—she will be fully recovered in a day or so, I expect.'

'A pretty child, I thought,' Maud ventured in a deceptively innocent tone, her fingers running idly over a marble statuette of Adonis that reposed on an inlaid ivory table.

'Very,' Jake said stiffly.

'You speak oddly, Jake,' she remarked. 'Do you dislike Miss Hythe?'

His control snapped. 'I did not come here to discuss Miss Hythe. And if it be your intention to harp on about her in this manner I shall bid you a very good night!'

Lady Matilda Ingleby was left to stare impotently at the door as it closed behind him, all her suspicions vibrantly alive.

If they are proved, she thought vengefully, someone will pay, trust me! Let them both beware!

CHAPTER TEN

THEODORE FARLEIGH, unlike his more somnolent companion, Harry Blaine, was an early riser. To exercise his mare in Hyde Park of a morning was his common practice. Although the more fashionable promenade took place in the late afternoon, there was always a number of acquaintances braving the chilly April morning.

Theo had enjoyed several interchanges already on this particular day when he heard himself hailed by a familiar female voice. Looking across the way, he saw an open carriage coming abreast of him, and in the fashionably dressed woman within he at once recognised Sothern's mistress.

'Good day to you, Lady Maud,' he called, intending to pass on. But, to his surprise, she beckoned. He urged his horse across the carriage-way, wondering if she was going to ask him when Lord Sothern would be returning. Not having seen him since the wedding, he would be unable to tell her.

But Lady Matilda was apparently uninterested in Jake's whereabouts. She conversed on commonplace topics for a moment or two, and Farleigh expected her then to move on, for there was a sharp wind blowing and she was obliged to hold her fashionable wide-brimmed and feathered hat for fear of its being snatched away. Mystified, he talked on. Then she introduced the subject occupying her mind.

'By the way, Farleigh, what has happened to that delightful child Lady Staplegrove introduced, do you know? She brought the girl with her to the Waldemar's rout, as I recall.'

'Clementina?' Theo asked unguardedly.

'Is that her name?'

'Yes. Clementina Hythe—or rather—I mean, yes, Hythe,' he said disjointedly, recalling his promise of silence on the matter of Clementina's recent change of name.

'Hythe?' repeated Lady Maud musingly, giving no sign that she had noticed Theo's hesitation. 'I think I have not heard the name. One of these northern families, perhaps?'

'Norfolk, actually. Though she has lately resided in Sussex with the Henlows—er—with an uncle.'

'Her parents are dead, then, I take it?'

'Oh, yes.'

'Poor child,' sighed Maud. 'So sad, at that age.'

'Yes, she has had an unhappy time of it,' agreed Theo, his mind on the past few days.

'I rather expected to see her going about with Lady Staplegrove, but she seems to have vanished.' And Maud tinkled with soft laughter.

'She is—er—she was——' Theo broke off, reddening uncomfortably as he realised that he could say nothing to the purpose. Belatedly, he had taken in that Lady Matilda was showing an uncommon interest in a girl with whom she was entirely unacquainted. Not having been present at the moment of Clementina's indiscreet reference to Maud at

Lady Waldemar's rout, he could have no notion of her ladyship's motive, though, considering the rumours that had been circulating at the time, he might guess. But he was no fool, and he realised at once that he had been skilfully pumped for information.

Her persistence in spite of the inclement weather was now explained. He had little liking for Lady Matilda, tolerating her only for Sothern's sake. Circumstances had altered, however. He did not think he was courting any danger now in having a little of his own back. Accordingly, he smiled with ironic charm at the lady.

'I am afraid I cannot answer you, Lady Maud. But you will doubtless obtain all the latest news of Miss Hythe if you care to call upon Lady Staplegrove.' Tipping his hat, Farleigh bowed and spurred his horse onward.

Lady Matilda might rage inwardly at the studied provocation of his last remark, for there was naturally no possibility of her calling upon the dowager. But she had gleaned enough to increase her suspicions to fever pitch.

So there *was* something between Jake and that wretched Hythe girl! As she had suspected, indeed. And Farleigh knew all about it. Blaine, too, doubtless. For a few moments she toyed with the idea of sounding out Sir Harry. Regretfully she rejected it. Blaine would be even more openly offensive than Farleigh if he realised what she was at, and for all he flirted with her she knew he had no serious *tendre*. What was more, Blaine would tell Jake. No, she could not risk it.

What else had she learned? Not much, she acknowledged regretfully. Then she recalled one of Theo's slips. Clementina had lately resided in Sussex with—now what was the name? Merrow? Henley? No, wait! Henlow. Surely that was it. Henlow. The name rang a vague bell. That must be why it had registered.

Casting about in her mind, she ran rapidly through her acquaintance. All at once she got it. A fair young man, startlingly good-looking. She had engineered an introduction at—where was it? Heavens yes, Lady Waldemar's! It all fitted.

The picture formed in her mind—the girl, Clementina, staring, ready to faint. The young man, Henlow, equally astonished. She had seen it all, for she had kept her eye close on Sothern once she had learned that the girl was a guest of Lady Staplegrove's. She had been uneasy from the first. And with good reason, it now appeared.

There was a mystery here. And Sothern was mixed up in it. It behoved her, she realised, to cultivate the young man, Henlow. Something to which she was in no way averse. He really had been a devastating creature. Now who was it who had introduced him?

While Lady Matilda Ingleby was busy seeking out information concerning her the erstwhile Miss Hythe in person was engaged at the breakfast table in a futile attempt to convince her hostess that she would do better to stay quite out of Society's eyes.

'For how will it look, ma'am, if I appear with you now, when once the secret of my marriage is out?'

'That is just what I have been trying to explain, silly child,' the dowager told her in exasperated tones, placing the coffee-pot down on the table with something of a snap.

'If you imagine that Jake will pretend to fall madly in love with me, all for Society's benefit, I am afraid you are doomed to disappointment,' Clementina said shrewdly, sipping her coffee. 'In all honesty, ma'am, can you see him making such a spectacle of himself?'

Lady Staplegrove snorted. She was spreading apricot preserve on her bread with a lavish hand. 'He did so over Maud Ingleby. He may very well do so over you.'

'I thank you, ma'am, I have no desire to be singled out in *that* fashion!'

'Oh, tush! You are as pig-headed as Sothern himself. I have had occasion to say so before this. I did not mean that, and you know it.'

Clementina heaved a heavy sigh, and added another lump of sugar to her coffee. 'I am sorry to disoblige you, ma'am.'

'My dear Clementina, it is not I you are disobliging, but yourself. Can you not see that tongues will wag cruelly otherwise?'

'I had rather they wagged against me than in favour of an insipid, romantical fairy-tale which does not even have the merit of being likely!' Clementina declared roundly, stirring her cup with furious energy.

Lady Staplegrove gave it up. 'Very well. I have done my best. Don't blame me when the tabbies cut you!'

Clementina laid down her spoon, put out her hand, and warmly clasped the dowager's fingers. She was chuckling.

'Dear ma'am, you are quite dreadful! You know very well that none would dare cut me when I make my appearance under your aegis.'

Lady Staplegrove acknowledged the truth of this with a brief, reluctant smile. For a moment she ate in silence.

'What, then, do you intend?' she asked at length.

'To keep out of sight.'

'I see. For how long?'

'Forever, if need be.'

'Highly practical!' snorted her ladyship. 'Have a little sense, Clementina, do.'

Clementina gave her a rueful look. 'Don't press me, ma'am. Not yet.' She sighed again, and picked up her sweetened cup of coffee. 'I suppose I must talk to Jake. I dare say we may come to some amicable arrangement.'

Lady Staplegrove frowned. 'You cannot end it, Clementina.'

'Not that, no. It is too late for that, I know. But, if we must inhabit the same house, go about in Society, perhaps we can agree terms that are mutually acceptable. We need not see a great deal of each other, after all, and—and Jake at least has other interests.'

There was much that the dowager might have said in repudiation of the bleak prospect thus outlined. But wisely she chose to hold her tongue. There was little likelihood, she reflected, of either of this volatile couple settling down in such bloodless companionship. She passed over a platter of bread and butter.

'Eat something, child. And think about all I have said. You may change your mind.'

At first Clementina had no notion of doing anything of the kind. But as the day wore on, bringing no sign of Jake, she began to feel restless. Her long sleep had refreshed her, although she still regarded the union with a jaundiced eye. But she was no longer the quivering bundle of yesterday, still weak from the after-effects of the drug and the excitements she had undergone. Feeling much more like her usual self, and having decided to discuss the situation sensibly with her new husband, she wanted, characteristically, to be up and doing.

When Jake put in no appearance she was initially piqued. But at his continued absence she grew incensed. The very least he could have done was to send a note if he did not mean to call. Besides, he ought to have called. Common courtesy demanded it.

By evening Clementina was so irate that she resolved, after all, to gratify the dowager and accompany her to the theatre. What was more, she would go as Miss Hythe. And his lordship, for all she cared, might go to the devil!

So it was that Lord Sothern, having spent the day in sulky determination to let her new young ladyship know that he did not care a damn for her outrageous conduct, saw from his position in the pit both his grandmother and his wife enter Lady Staplegrove's box at Drury Lane.

So began this ridiculous farce, he thought savagely. Well, if either one of them expected him to portray the nauseous role of moonstruck lover they had better think again.

But Sir Harry Blaine, who had accompanied him here, was nudging him in the ribs.

'Better bring me up to date, old fellow,' he murmured. 'Am I to keep mum, or do I address the lady as she's entitled?'

Sothern's eyes were on Clementina as she made sure that the dowager was comfortable before settling into her own chair. He noted, with quite irrational annoyance, that she had chosen to wear an exceptionally pretty gown of a strong green more suited to a married woman than the young débutante she was supposedly portraying.

'Stay put and you won't have to address her at all,' he told Blaine shortly.

'By God, man, what do you take me for?' uttered the other, shocked. 'Wouldn't be guilty of such discourtesy for any money. Of course I must pay my respects!'

Jake swore under his breath. 'Very well. *Hythe*, then, if you must. My grandmother is engaged on some idiotic charade to avert a scandal.'

'Very sensible,' approved Sir Harry. 'Just what one would expect.' He began to move away, and looked back. 'You coming, Jake?'

About to refuse, the Earl caught his friend's eye. Harry was clearly expecting him to go too. An excuse would make him seem churlish, and perhaps give rise to speculation in Blaine's mind. However he felt, Jake realised that it would be most improper to permit his friend to become aware of his marital difficulties.

Accordingly, both gentlemen were very soon knocking on the door of Lady Staplegrove's box. Some friends of her ladyship's had arrived before them, and the small box was already full. The dowager was the first to notice her grandson's entry.

'Good *evening*, Sothern,' she said pleasantly. By that slight emphasis and a lift of her expressive brows she gave Jake to understand that his absence that day had displeased her.

He caught the faint gasp that escaped his wife's lips, and, having greeted his grandmother, he leaned forward to peer over the shoulders of the two ladies who obscured his view of her. He was accorded one brief glimpse of those green eyes as Clementina sought and found his face. Then she pointedly turned to speak to the lady on her other side. Thereafter her profile was all he was permitted to gaze upon.

Although to all outward appearance Clementina was perfectly calm, in fact her heart hammered uncomfortably in her breast. At the unexpected sound of his voice it had jerked violently and, not trusting herself to speak, she had elected to ignore his lordship instead.

Not to be outdone in the matter of incivility, Jake passed over the claims of anyone present to his attention, and his glance raked the boxes on the other side of the house. In one of them he saw his mistress. She was looking straight at him. Their eyes met. She smiled and beckoned. Jake nodded. Then he turned to his grandmother.

'Forgive me, ma'am. I came only to pay my respects.' He bowed, and then glanced at Clementina. 'Your servant, Miss Hythe.'

Clementina, who for all her apparent unconcern had been covertly watching her husband, was an indignant witness to his silent exchange with Maud. How dared he insult her so? Even if their marriage was secret, he had no right to acknowledge his mistress while in his wife's company.

As he spoke her head turned. Slowly her eyes raked the length of his body and rested on his face, the whole gesture eloquent of contempt. She saw his cheeks darken, and was satisfied.

'Oh, are you leaving us already?' she said, in a voice totally devoid of interest. 'What a pity! Goodnight, Lord Sothern.' Then she turned away.

Jake abruptly left the box, aware of his grandmother's amused smile and the eager curiosity on the faces of her guests. Sir Harry, having made his own farewells, caught him up in the corridor.

'I say, old fellow. What the devil was all that about?'

Sothern ground his teeth.

'That,' he grated, quite forgetting his earlier concern at the impropriety of discussing his marital problems with Blaine, 'was a sample of my *wife's* company manners.'

'Can't say I blame her,' said his friend frankly. 'Couldn't expect her to take it when you flaunt your indiscretions in her face, you know.'

'I would not have done so had she not treated me to a display of blatant incivility.'

'Six of one and half a dozen of the other, if you ask me.'

'I don't ask you!'

'No need to snap my nose off, old fellow. You knew what she was when you married the girl. Showed us what she was made of that very first night, by God!'

Jake did not reply. Harry was right, he knew, well aware that he had brought his own discomfiture on himself. The knowledge did not make him any the less furious, however. It was therefore in a mood of seething resentment that he entered Lady Matilda Ingleby's box. While he responded to her delighted greeting, he could not forbear casting surreptitious glances at his grandmother's box opposite.

The action of the farce was beginning on stage, and the visitors were leaving. He could see that his bride and Lady Staplegrove had their heads together. Doubtless they were discussing him. Not in any kindly spirit, he dared swear. Damn it to hell! This whole affair was intolerable.

'Miss Hythe is recovered, I see,' remarked Lady Maud in his ear. 'Does she stay long in company with your grandmother?'

If the interchange between himself and Clementina had angered him, it galled him even more to hear her referred to as Miss Hythe. Especially by his mistress, on whose lips, he decided suddenly, Clementina's name was a profanity. Sudden remorse hit him. What the devil was he doing here? Harry *was* right. He had offered his wife an unspeakable insult.

He looked at Lady Matilda, and the dark eyes smouldered. His voice was even, but deadly.

'I don't ever want to hear you speak of her again. You are unworthy to mention her name. And, God help me, while I am with you, so am I!'

So saying, he rose from his seat and left her.

Rigid with wrath, Lady Maud resolved to have her revenge. The means, she was convinced, would shortly be in her power. Her hand reached into her reticule and fingered the note she had received in response to her message to young Ellis Henlow.

Having opened the front door to his mistress and her young guest, Dorridge coughed discreetly. Lady Staplegrove paused in her way to the stairs, and turned to look at him, brows raised.

'You have something to tell me, Dorridge?'

The butler bowed. 'His lordship, my lady,' he said apologetically. 'I did venture to suggest that the hour was too far advanced for a visit, my lady, but his lordship——'

'His lordship,' said a voice from the doorway of the pink parlour, 'insisted on waiting for you.'

'Sothern!' ejaculated the dowager, swinging round to stare at her grandson. 'What a start you gave me! What do you here at such an hour?'

'I am here,' asserted Jake, coming forward into the light, 'to see my wife.'

His eyes were on Clementina as he spoke. She was standing stock still in the middle of the hall, her pose rigid.

'Oh, Sothern, you *fool*!' uttered Lady Staplegrove in exasperated accents.

'I fail to understand what is so foolish in wanting to speak with my bride.'

'I am not talking of that,' said his grandmother scoffingly. 'But if you mean to speak so openly we shall be quite undone.' She glanced significantly at the butler.

'Oh, Dorridge will keep his mouth shut, never fear,' insisted Jake cheerfully. 'Eh, Dorridge?'

'I beg your lordship's pardon,' said the butler with stately dignity, 'but I fear I am growing rather deaf.'

'Admirable, Dorridge, admirable. You hear, Grandmama?'

'There is nothing wrong with *my* hearing,' replied her ladyship tartly. 'I don't need you to assure me of my butler's discretion. Yours is what concerns me.'

She nodded to Dorridge, who discreetly withdrew.

'Now then, Sothern. It is late, and we are tired. Say what you have to say, and go.'

Clementina made a move to go to her, but Jake stepped forward and grasped her wrist.

'No, you don't! I came for a word with you, and I am going to have it!'

'Let me go at once!' Clementina ordered, tugging against his hold.

'In a moment,' Jake said, and led her willy-nilly to the pink parlour.

'Really, Sothern!' protested his grandmother, moving to intercept him. 'Your conduct goes from bad to worse. Let her go!'

'Grandmama, if you please,' Jake said politely, and put her gently aside.

He then drew Clementina into the parlour and firmly closed the door in Lady Staplegrove's face. Then he let go of his wife's wrist, and leaned against the door.

'Quite like old times,' he commented, smiling a little. 'Only I trust you will not resort to a candlestick on this occasion?'

There was no answering smile from Clementina. She moved slowly to the centre of the parlour, and turned to face him, hugging her taffeta cloak about her as if for protection.

'Well, sir?'

Jake regarded her dumbly. He had lit candles in the wall-sconces, and there were branches on both the mantelpiece and the side-table. Candlelight played over her features, and touched the red in her hair to streaks of fire.

'You are…exceedingly beautiful,' he said softly.

Clementina's lip trembled, and her heart began to beat an irregular tattoo. She felt her cheeks grow hot, and swallowed on a dry throat. Then she remembered how he had behaved at the theatre.

'I must suppose,' she began as evenly as she could, 'that you did not drag me in here to listen to empty compliments?'

Jake frowned. 'Empty?'

'You forget. I know what constitutes your idea of beauty. It is as unlike me as it is possible to be.'

'Quite unlike,' he agreed. 'But a man may admire more than one type of beauty.'

'May he indeed?' said Clementina in a trembling tone. 'And desire to possess it, too, I dare say.'

He took a step towards her. 'Clementina, you don't understand.'

She backed away. 'Oh, yes. I understand only too well. Let us have done with pretence and veiled remarks.'

'By all means,' Jake said swiftly. 'You are angry, and I don't blame you.'

'Generous!'

'Please. Let me speak. What I did tonight was abhorrent. I know it. I am come to beg your forgiveness.'

Clementina bit her lip. She looked away. 'Very well.'

Jake made a move towards her, and she turned quickly and held up a hand.

'You are absolved,' she said, low-voiced, 'for acknowledging your mistress in my presence. But that does not mean that you are at liberty to—to touch me.'

Jake flinched back as if she had slapped him. His eyes glittered. 'I think you had better explain that remark.'

'Do I need to?' Clementina flashed suddenly.

'As I have not the remotest conjecture what it means,' Jake said, jerking out the words, 'I think you do, yes.'

'I had not thought you obtuse,' Clementina remarked sarcastically. 'However, since you will have it in plain words——'

'Plain words will be most welcome,' he snapped.

'In plain words, then,' she said furiously, 'your wife has no intention, my lord Sothern, of sharing your favours with your mistress!'

Jake's eyes narrowed. 'Is that an ultimatum?'

'It is a simple statement of fact.'

His lip curled. 'You have an odd idea of marriage.'

Clementina tossed her head. 'Oh, you need not think I don't know what is expected of me in this situation. A gently bred girl pretends to know nothing of her husband's amatory adventures.'

'A gently bred girl does not wander the streets in men's clothing, either,' he returned drily.

'There you are, then!' she exclaimed triumphantly.

'Oh, for God's sake! We are married. For how long do you think you can hold out against me? You are merely using Maud as an excuse.'

Clementina breathed deeply once or twice. 'Let us get one thing clear, my lord. This marriage was foisted upon me. If you wanted a complaisant wife you should have chosen elsewhere. I told you once before that I would never cuckold Jeremy. By the same token I would have known that, whatever else might be my fate with him, at the very least I could have expected a like respect. With you the matter is entirely different. I know I have no power to change your accustomed way of life. Indeed, I—I have no desire to do so. You may go your way. But do me the courtesy to remain aloof from me. For I cannot and will not be humiliated so.'

A smile glimmered on his lordship's lips, but it was not reflected in his eyes.

'And what of my heirs?' he asked, deceptively cool.

Clementina flushed. 'There will be none! You should have thought of that before you acted with such quixotic impetuosity.'

'"Quixotic impetuosity"! A fine phrase. And a fine speech.'

He walked forward until he stood close before her. His hand reached out to cup her chin, forcing her to look at him.

'Words, Clementina,' he said softly. 'Just words. You know as well as I that if I choose to claim my rights you will not fight me.'

She stared up at him, her eyes defiant. But her lip trembled.

'You—you won't force me,' she whispered. 'I know that.'

'I won't have to. I have not forgotten how you responded to me yesterday morning.'

'I d-didn't respond!'

His eyebrow lifted. 'Oh? Then how is it that I felt with you even as I might with some Covent Garden jade?'

Clementina gasped. Eyes blazing, she wrenched herself away, and her hand came up to slap his cheek, hard.

'You little fiend!' he uttered, stepping smartly out of her way.

'How *dare* you?' Clementina cried throbbingly. 'How dare you say such a thing of me? Get away! Get out of my sight! I never want to see you again as long as I live!'

'Certainly I shall go,' Jake said, his eyes snapping. 'But permit me to recommend that you try for some self-command, you little termagant.'

'Go *away*!'

'Your passions are quite uncontrolled, my child. *In* bed or out!'

'Get out! Get out! I hate you!' raged Clementina and, looking about her, she snatched a small ornament from the mantelpiece and threw it at him, missing by inches.

'Ye gods!' Jake ejaculated, and made for the door as he saw her reaching for another.

As he closed the door behind him, with more haste than grace, he heard something shatter against it.

'God damn the little shrew!' he uttered furiously, and with swift steps he crossed to the front door and opened it. He hesitated, listening, but there was only silence from the pink parlour.

'Hell and the devil confound her!' he swore. 'No, I won't go back!'

He stepped outside and firmly shut the front door behind him. Then he was down the steps and walking away into the night, quite failing to notice the coach drawn up a little way down the street.

Inside it, one of its occupants watched him out of sight.

CHAPTER ELEVEN

LEFT alone, Clementina stood panting, glaring at the unresponsive door. In a minute or two her temper began to cool, and she gazed in consternation at the fragments of china lying all over the carpet. With a sense of shock she realised what she had done. Worse, she recalled what she had said.

'Dear Lord!' she whispered. 'I didn't mean it. I didn't mean it, Jake!'

Shaking, she moved to a chair and sat down. She felt ashamed. He had said a terrible thing. But, God help her, it was true! She had responded to his lovemaking. Like any whore, she had squirmed and writhed in ecstasy. And she had had no idea of there being anything wrong. Nor had Jake. She knew he had enjoyed her as much as she had revelled in his passion.

She put up her hands to cover her face, aware that more than anything else she wanted to feel that passion again. To have Jake's arms about her, to feel his lips on hers, his hands moving over her limbs, lighting that flame that only he could quench.

When the knocking came on the front door she jumped as if she had been shot. Then, with a glad cry, she rose quickly and darted out of the room to fling wide the front door.

'Jake?'

Clementina stopped short, her heart jarring to a stop. Her cousin Jeremy stood on the doorstep.

'Jeremy!' she gasped. 'What are you doing here? How did you come? And so late!'

Her cousin blinked at the hail of words, his mouth opening and shutting uselessly as he strove to make sense of them. Clementina saw his confusion, and pulled herself together.

'You had better come in, Jeremy.'

As he made no move, she reached out and caught his coat-sleeve, pulling him through the door. She shut it behind him.

'Now, Jeremy. Why have you come? How did you find me?'

'H-Hackney,' the young man uttered, removing his hat. 'C-came in a hackney cab.'

'Yes, yes, very well. But why?' demanded Clementina impatiently.

His mouth quivered. 'D-don't be angry, C-Clemmy. P-please. Don't be angry.'

With some difficulty Clementina swallowed her own natural agitation and forced herself to speak calmly, infusing warmth into her voice. 'I'm not angry, Jeremy. Not with you.'

She took his hand and drew him gently into the pink parlour, where they might converse without waking the household, although she doubted that Lady Staplegrove was as yet asleep.

'What is it, Jeremy? Tell me.'

'You help me, C-Clemmy. Help me?'

'Of course I will help you,' she assured him, pushing him into a chair. 'Only sit quietly and tell me what is the matter.'

He twisted his hat in his hands, and his eyes were troubled. 'Don't know. Don't understand. Mama said there's no money. No money for me. Said you help me.'

The green eyes narrowed suspiciously. 'Did your mama send you here?'

He shook his head vigorously. 'Not M-Mama.'

'Your papa, then?'

'Not Papa. Papa said Dunhythe is mine. S-said he look after Dunhythe when he comes back. You l-look after me.'

'But I *can't*,' Clementina said unguardedly. 'Not now.'

His eyes gazed sadly upon her. 'You c-can't help me?'

She sighed. 'Yes, Jeremy. I can help you. At least, I think so. I can't look after you, though. Your mama will do that.' She saw the hurt and doubt in his face, and stroked his hair, much as she might stroke an injured puppy. 'Don't worry, Jeremy. You'll be all right. I'll help you. The money will be sorted out.'

She moved away from him to the fireplace, thinking. Now that she was married she did not know precisely how her affairs stood. In the normal way, all financial arrangements would have been settled between her family lawyer and that of her prospective husband. But as things were there had been no preliminary negotiations, and she had no idea what rights, if any, she might have over her inheritance, or what part of it had passed directly into Sothern's hands.

She must consult with Cullen. Jake, too, perhaps. At present, however, there could be no discussion with her husband. Well, there was nothing to prevent her seeing Cullen first. She turned back to Jeremy.

'Where are you staying, Jeremy? At a hotel?'

'Coaching-house,' he told her briefly.

'Good. Then you must go back there now.'

She began painstakingly to explain what she wanted him to do, too preoccupied to wonder how her aunt could have been so careless and imprudent as to allow him to come to London apparently quite alone.

'You will come back here in the morning, Jeremy. Do you understand?'

'Back here in the m-morning,' he repeated, nodding slowly.

'Together we will go to Mr Cullen and find out how I can help you.'

He looked somewhat bemused, but grasped gratefully at the last words. 'You help me, C-Clemmy?'

'Yes, I will help you. Tomorrow. Come here at ten o'clock. Ten o'clock, mind.'

He repeated the time to show that he had understood, and made no protest as she ushered him out into the night.

Clementina went slowly up the stairs, compassion for her cousin causing her to feel some guilt

that in her own turmoil she had not given a thought
to his sorry situation. There was Margery to be
thought of, too. Really, she had been abominably
selfish!

Stupid, too. For here she was in a situation as
fortunate as it was unexpected, and all she could
think about was her own misery. She ought to be
perfectly content. She was a countess now. Lady
Sothern. With a house in town, an estate in the
country, and goodness knows what besides! All the
elegancies of life that wealth and position might
afford. And yet she dared to bewail her lot. How
many wives of her class had the good fortune to be
loved by their husbands? Was she asking too much?

'Clementina!'

The harshly whispered syllables interrupted her
thoughts, and she jumped. She looked up quickly
to see Lady Staplegrove in her peacock-decorated
dressing-gown standing at the head of the stairs.
Clementina hurried up to her.

'Dear ma'am, you should be in bed,' she uttered
in a hushed tone. 'What can you be thinking of,
standing out here in the cold?'

'Don't fuss, child,' the dowager said testily. 'How
do you imagine I could sleep with you and Sothern
spitting at each other down there? Has he but just
gone?'

'Oh, no. He left some time ago. It was my cousin
Jeremy who just left.'

'What, the simpleton? What in the world was he
doing here?'

As Clementina explained she inexorably but gently eased Lady Staplegrove back into her bed-chamber and tucked her into bed.

'Will you stop mothering me, you foolish child?' the old lady protested. 'Don't think you can flummery me into forgetting my purpose. What passed between you two? Tell me at once.'

Clementina sighed, and sat down on the edge of the bed. She knew very well that Lady Staplegrove was not speaking of Jeremy's visit.

'We quarrelled, of course, ma'am. What else?'

'Lord above, I know that! Do you take me for a nincompoop?'

'Far from it, ma'am,' Clementina said, smiling.

'Then answer me, girl, do.'

'What can I say? He offered me an apology, which I accepted. Then he offered me an insult, and I lost my temper. I'm afraid I have broken several of your china ornaments,' she confessed ruefully.

Lady Staplegrove's eyes twinkled. 'As long as they found their mark I don't mind in the least.'

Clementina gave a reluctant chuckle. 'They did not, ma'am. I have a poor aim.'

'A pity.'

Silence fell. After a moment the dowager reached out and covered the girl's hand with her own. 'A penny for them, child.'

Clementina looked at her, and shrugged slightly. A pathetic smile wavered on her lips.

'I have been thinking how silly I have been, dear ma'am. Jake has offered—indeed, given—me so much. What right have I to ask for the impossible?'

'Ah.' Her ladyship leaned back against her pillows and regarded the piquant face steadily, her expression unreadable. 'So you feel you are baying for the moon?'

'Well, ma'am, you know Jake. And there is Lady Matilda...'

'That woman!' The dowager snorted. 'Don't speak of her to me! I can't abide the wench.' She regarded Clementina smoulderingly. 'So you mean to let her have him—without a fight?'

Clementina stiffened. 'I will not sue for Jake's attentions. Nor enter into competition with—with a woman of her kind. Not with any woman. If I can't have him to myself, then I don't want him at all.'

'Bravo!' applauded the dowager. 'And thank the Lord! I was beginning to think you had lost that spirit I so much admire.' She patted the girl's hand. 'But now to business. This matter of your cousin's finances had better be left to Jake and Cullen, you know. I am sure between them they will settle all satisfactorily.'

'No doubt. But I prefer to deal with it myself. I may be married to your grandson, ma'am, but I do not admit of his right to order my affairs as he sees fit. I shall speak to Cullen myself.'

With which, Clementina bade Lady Staplegrove goodnight, and left the room with head held high, leaving the dowager in some glee at her own adroit manipulation of her young protégée's emotions. Apathy was of no use to anyone, she felt. And how little it had taken to sting the girl into defiance!

How good it was to be old! What fun to be wise for the young, who were so unable to be wise for themselves. That darling child! Her grandson was a fortunate man.

On this satisfactory thought the dowager drifted into sleep.

It was a good while before Clementina realised that the hackney cab was taking an uncommonly long time to arrive at their destination.

She had given Mr Cullen's directions to the coachman herself, and had been occupied for some time in carefully explaining her position to Jeremy. It had proved very difficult to instil into his head any idea of the complication that had arisen in their mutual affairs as a result of her change of status.

Apart from the fact that he could not grasp what she was trying to tell him he seemed unusually agitated. Clementina was just about to enquire into his state of mind when she suddenly noticed that they were crossing over water.

'What in the world——?' she exclaimed, and leaned forward to peer from the window.

Over the walled edges of a bridge her startled eyes took in the silvery sheen of the Thames with its heavy traffic: barges laden with goods, probably recently unloaded from ships in the port of London and beginning their long journey inland; a longboat pulled by a dozen oarsmen in naval uniform;

watermen ferrying passengers afoot from one bank to the other; and a number of rowboats carrying their human cargo on God knew what legitimate business!

Clementina turned an incredulous gaze on her cousin. 'Jeremy, what is happening? Where are we going?'

He gaped at her unhappily. 'C-Cullen. Going to see Cullen.'

'But Mr Cullen's place of business is in the City,' she protested. 'Why must we cross the river? We are going south.'

Jeremy's jaw rose and fell in that vacant way he had when nonplussed. Clementina frowned as a tingle of apprehension ran down her spine.

'The coachman cannot have mistaken the way, can he?' she murmured, half to herself, trying to find some legitimate reason for the error in order to quell her growing disquiet.

She looked again at her cousin, and read discomfiture mingled with his usual air of confusion.

'Jeremy!' she said sternly, and he quailed. 'Where are we going?'

Miserably he shook his head. 'Don't know.'

'But you knew we were not going to Cullen.'

'G-going to C-Cullen with you, C-Clemmy,' he uttered, nodding furiously.

'*No!* You meant all the time to take me elsewhere. You will tell me this instant. *Where are we going?*'

He cowered away before her fury. 'Don't *know*,' he almost wailed. 'He s-said—he s-said——'

'Who said?'

Jeremy collapsed into frightened whimpering. Belatedly it came to Clementina that it was highly unlikely that he would have been allowed to come to London alone. Staying at an inn, too. Who was with him, then? If not his mama or papa...

At this moment the carriage began to slow down. Clementina looked out of the window, a lively fear making her breath short. She noticed at once the hoardings outside a large building they were passing to her right, on which colourful posters advertised Astley's Amphitheatre. Then it must have been Westminster Bridge, she thought at once, for, as everyone knew, the equestrian circus was situated in Lambeth.

As she realised this the hackney turned off the road and came to rest in the yard of a small inn. From the doorway a familiar figure stepped out and moved towards the coach. Clementina gasped and shrank back.

The hackney door was wrenched open. The grimly smiling features of Ellis Henlow looked in at her.

'Well met, dear cousin.'

'You!' Clementina uttered faintly.

'Yes, it is I, cousin. Step down, if you please.'

'I don't please,' Clementina said in a shaking voice, adding with returning spirit, 'and I am not your cousin, I thank God!'

Ellis's tone hardened. 'Step down. Now!' He leaned into the coach, raising a clenched fist as though he would strike her.

Clementina looked wildly round, seeking some means of assistance. Jeremy still cowered away in his corner of the coach, his frightened eyes glued on his half-brother in a look compounded of fear and bewilderment. There was no help there, she knew, realising in the same instant how Ellis must have terrorised her cousin into tricking her. She thought fleetingly of Jake, and a wave of hopeless misery shook her.

Blindly she pushed at Ellis Henlow's upraised fist, and moved forward to descend from the carriage into the inn yard. There was a light chaise standing ready, a team of horses harnessed to it. Henlow grasped her arm in an ungentle grip and forced her steps towards this equipage.

She thought how like him it was to waste money on four horses where two would suffice. For who was to pursue them to wherever it was he meant to take her? Lady Staplegrove might worry when she did not reappear. And Jake—Jake would merely assume that she had run away again.

Ellis pushed her into the chaise and shut the door on her. For a moment she thought perhaps he was not coming with her. That would make it easier to escape. Then she saw the hackney carriage moving off, and realised that he had merely gone to get rid of his brother.

He was returning with swift steps to the chaise, his caped overcoat swinging about his legs. She gathered her failing spirits together. She must not be weak now. He was a dangerous man, a violent man. All her dependence lay in her own wits. The first essential was to keep his temper even.

Ellis jumped lightly into the chaise, and took his place beside her. The carriage began to move.

'Where are you taking me?' Clementina asked, an audible quaver in her voice that was not entirely feigned.

'Portsmouth,' he answered shortly. 'For the moment.'

'Portsmouth?' she repeated, stunned.

For a moment she could not take it in. Then thoughts began to jostle one another in her head. Portsmouth. Dear Lord! It must be all of sixty or seventy miles away. They would be travelling all day. Was he mad? How could she get word to Jake? And why Portsmouth, of all places? *She must escape.* What would her kind benefactress think of this latest exploit? Heaven help her, but this time she was truly not to blame! But Portsmouth!

All the while, from the plate-glass window before her, her absent gaze was fixed on the yellow-liveried back of the post-boy bobbing up and down on the lead horse—'for all the world like a bouncing wave'.

The thought floated into the incoherent jumble of her brain, and she suddenly sat bolt upright.

'Portsmouth!' she ejaculated, understanding coming in a flash. 'Then you mean to take me abroad?'

'If all else fails, yes,' he agreed curtly.

She stared at him, bewildered, as the gathering fear knotted her stomach. Then she looked out of the window, glancing feverishly about, hardly knowing that she did so.

The buildings were thinning out as they left London behind. Green fields with peacefully grazing cattle and sheep met her eyes, interspersed here and there with a clutch of village houses or the spire of a church, now and again a glimpse of some large country mansion through the trees. They passed a drover with a gaggle of geese on their way to market and a slow, lumbering covered wagon.

The post-boy's horn blasted, startling Clementina into full awareness as the chaise slowed up for the Robin Hood gate. She watched the pike-keeper pull the gate wide, and a sense of hopelessness began to invade her as the carriage passed through.

She looked piteously at her captor, almost unconsciously assuming an even more downcast mien than her true feelings warranted, knowing this would serve her best with this man. Defiance would only anger him.

'In God's name, Ellis, why are you doing this?'

He deigned no reply, keeping his eyes on the road ahead, but a muscle twitched in his cheek, and she saw his hands in their York Tan gloves clench a little.

'I don't understand,' she uttered, exaggerating the plaintive note. 'How can this kidnap avail you? I am Sothern's wife. What hope can you possibly have of gaining command of my inheritance?'

He turned to her, his handsome face marred by a sneer. 'Do you take me for a fool? Of course I know that.'

'Then why? Revenge? Do you hate me so much?'

'Hate? I?' He gave a scornful laugh. 'I don't feel anything at all for you, my *lady*.' He laid ironic stress on the last word.

'Jake, then,' Clementina said at once. 'You are doing it to revenge yourself on Jake?'

'There is an element of that, yes. He spoiled my schemes, and I don't care for that.'

'Then—then if it is not all revenge, what do you hope to gain? What can you possibly gain?' Clementina paused, watching the fine profile beside her. Ellis was smiling, an unpleasant smile. The thought struck her so forcibly that she forgot her pose.

'Ransom!' she exclaimed. 'You mean to hold me to ransom.' A brittle laugh escaped her. 'Dear Lord, Ellis! I had thought you had more sense than to engage in criminal activity. You may well get money out of Sothern to recover me safe and sound. But after. Have you thought of that? You can't believe that Jake will not use the full panoply of the law against you?'

Ellis was unmoved. He showed all his teeth in a smug grin. 'Oh, he won't do that.'

'You must be mad to think so!' Clementina told him fiercely. 'The Earl of Sothern allow himself to be bled and the culprit go unpunished? You will be hanged for an abductor and kidnapper, Ellis Henlow!'

'And what will the Earl of Sothern do about the scandal surrounding his wife?'

Clementina gasped in sudden shock. 'You mean——?'

'I mean, dear Lady Sothern,' said Ellis, supremely confident, 'that Sothern will not be so foolish as to make public such a scandal. Once he goes to the law the business becomes known. And once it is known that her ladyship spent the night in the same room as her abductor...' He stopped, spreading his hands in a gesture of fatalism.

Clementina felt sick. True or not, such a story would ruin her in Society's eyes. A lady might survive an indiscretion conducted strictly within the ranks of the upper echelon of the fashionable world. But the shame and embarrassment of a publicly acknowledged abduction would close all doors to her. Sothern might even be forced to divorce her. Or, at the very least, to arrange a separation. On that thought a pang of such acute anguish shot through her that it was a moment or two before she remembered the one ray of light in all this deepening gloom. Insensibly it strengthened her, and her voice was rock steady when she spoke.

'You have miscalculated, Ellis. No one knows yet of our marriage. You will be laid by the heels before ever anyone in Society hears of it. You had better let me go at once and save yourself a good deal of trouble.'

'Had I now?' His eyes gleamed as he looked at her. 'You must think me improvident. I regret, Clementina, that it is you who are under a misapprehension. My fault. I forgot to mention it. By now the Hyde Park saunterers will be enjoying the very latest titbit of gossip. Hot from the lips of the one person whom they are certain must know the truth.'

CHAPTER TWELVE

LADY MATILDA INGLEBY had been cunning. Livid with wrath at Ellis Henlow's startling disclosure she might be. But no amount of jealousy would serve to make her lose sight of the main chance. She would not look the fool for any man. She it was who had attached Sothern to her. She must make it appear that the end of the affair was also her doing.

As it was, she decided vengefully. After all, there had been no precise definition of an end between them. As there might have been had he dealt honorably with her. The memory of her interview with Ellis Henlow rose up again, and she felt a resurgence of the all-consuming rage that had engulfed her at his words.

'Married? They were *married*!' she had uttered, disbelievingly. 'How is this possible? When were they married?'

'The day before yesterday,' Ellis had told her, his own feelings on the matter beggaring description.

He'd spoken, however, with a cool unconcern, his only interest in her reaction born of an in-built desire to turn everything to his own profit. How this woman's involvement might benefit him he was not yet able to see. But he was not one to waste opportunity. And opportunity he had felt there must be in an invitation from Sothern's mistress. So indeed it had proved.

'How do you know this, man?' had demanded Lady Maud, a hiss in her voice that spoke more eloquently than any words the nature of the blow this news had dealt her.

'Oh, I was there,' Ellis said offhandedly, paltering somewhat with the exact truth. 'I am family, you know. It was all rather sudden.'

Sudden? Aye, that was the *mot juste*. So sudden that it now hit her with stunning force. Her lover had married in the teeth of his mistress. And had come to her, lying of a lack of a rival, straight from his young wife's arms. *And he had said nothing*. God in heaven, was she not entitled to some consideration? She, who had shared his caresses, had given freely of herself to comfort his lonely nights, had offered him her all, only to be insulted at the last with his slighting comment which she had done nothing to deserve?

Conveniently forgetting how she had lured the Earl to her bed, as she had lured others before him—and even during his supposed tenancy, if the truth were told—Lady Matilda ranted and raved in the privacy of her boudoir. Never mind that her favours had been offered for her own satisfaction as well as his, that even tonight's encounter had been arranged with an eye to supplanting him with a younger and more personable comforter for her bed. He had no right to make that unutterably despicable remark that he had dared to allow to leave his lips at the theatre.

Unworthy to mention the girl's name, was she? They would see about that. She would mention it to some purpose, trust her!

Skilfully she planted her story. Her chosen confidante, the biggest gossip in town, learned from an apparently delighted Lady Maud that the Earl's own grandmother's scheming had saved her the disheartening task of bidding him a long-overdue farewell.

'I had long since tired of him, but what would you? Men are such sensitive creatures, my dear, and one hesitates to wound their excessive pride.'

'Oh, indeed!' gushed the lady, avidly drinking in the tale. 'And so how did it all end?'

'How it always does, naturally. When so determined a woman as Lady Staplegrove sets a matrimonial trap the outcome is inevitable. She contrived it so that the girl was hopelessly compromised, of course.'

'But how? In what situation did she place them?'

'Ah, that I am not at liberty to disclose,' Lady Matilda said intriguingly.

She hinted at a runaway match with the Earl in hot pursuit. Restoring the girl to her guardians, Sothern found his conduct open to question, for the guardians knew nothing of any other man. There was nothing for it but marriage, and that right speedily.

Lady Matilda did not, of course, phrase the story so plainly. It was rather the detail hinted at, but so painstakingly left out, that gave her auditor to understand it so.

By the time Sothern himself came riding to the park to exercise his horse the fashionable promenade was buzzing with the now thoroughly exaggerated tale, embellished as each teller of it thought fit. It did not take many minutes for him to realise that he was the subject of a general speculation, several persons twitting him slyly on his supposed misfortune, one even going so far as to congratulate him—not on his recent nuptials, but on his fortunate release from the clutches of Lady Matilda Ingleby.

Jake stared at this gentleman in speechless indignation. Realising his error, the other reddened, muttered a confused apology, and circumspectly withdrew. Seething, Jake kept an eye out for his two best friends, assuming at once that one of them must be the author of this blatant indiscretion.

He had spent most of the night tossing and turning, unable to sleep, fighting the urge to get up out of his bed, go back to Brook Street, and settle this nonsense with Clementina once and for all. The thought that such a show-down must of necessity take place in her bed where she now slept—alone—served only to increase his unrest.

He awoke little refreshed, a prey to an unprecedented tumult of emotion. In the confusion of violent longings, frustrations and anger, the distress and hurt, he discovered to his surprise that misery was uppermost. More than anything he wanted to see Clementina smile at him with more in her eyes than mere pleasure at his touch. She was his, yes. But, for all that he had possessed her, he could not reach her heart. Cursing himself, he recalled again and again the gap of long years that separated them. He could not rid himself of the memory of how she had spoken that very first night.

'You are far too old.'

Old? He was doting! Sighing over a chit of a girl, when he could have any woman he wanted for the taking. He pushed aside the thought that he did not want any other woman, and determined to die before he sued for her affections like a moonstruck boy.

But once in the Park he no sooner learned that their secret was out than all reason fled before his fury. The more so because Clementina must be hurt by the talk. He cared nothing for himself. People had been whispering about him all his adult life. But that they should dare to bandy his wife's name roused him to such a pitch of wrath as he had never known before.

Not seeing his two traitorous friends, he left the Park and discovered them at Brooks. Hustling them into a small writing-room, he barely waited to shut the door before rounding on them both.

'Fine friends I have! Which of you saw fit to blazon the story of my marriage abroad, may I ask? Whose tongue have I to thank for this base act of betrayal? Be sure you shall answer for it, either of you!'

Sir Harry Blaine went red in the face and began to bluster. 'By God, Sothern—by God! For what do you take me? How dare you accuse me—*me*!

By God, if I don't cut your liver out for this unspeakable insult...!'

'Wait, Harry!' Theo Farleigh intervened quickly. 'Calm yourself, I beg.'

'Calm myself? *Calm myself?*'

He squared up to Jake, and Theo pushed between them.

'Stop! You are under a misapprehension, both of you.'

As one, they turned on him.

'So it was you...'

'By God, Farleigh, you traitorous dog!'

'Hold there!' Theo shouted. 'I'm not your man. You fool, Jake! You too, Harry, to be so blind. Can't you see the fellow is too much beside himself to think clearly?'

Harry's head snapped round to stare at Sothern, suddenly intent. 'By God, you're right, Theo! Now then, Jake, take care. You warn me of apoplexy often enough. Look out for yourself, that's all I say. Look out!'

'Oh, be quiet, Harry!' Theo chided, quite exasperated. He took Sothern by the arm and shook it gently. 'My friend, I'll take my oath I know where this leak originates.' Then he proceeded to tell his friend about his meeting with Lady Matilda. 'How she found out the facts I don't know. But I'll lay my life she's at the root of it!'

'Maud? But she can't be,' Jake protested. 'She has no knowledge of any of it.'

'Ask her,' Theo advised.

'Yes,' agreed Blaine. 'I'll warrant you'll know how to get it out of the woman.'

Jake ground his teeth. 'If there's any truth in this I'll choke it out of her!'

With a brief apology for doubting his friends, he departed. At Half Moon Street the butler denied him entrance, saying that Lady Matilda was not at home.

'Is she not, indeed?' Jake said dangerously. 'I'll see for myself!'

So saying, he pushed past the butler, ran up the stairs, and flung open the door to the boudoir where Maud was wont to receive him.

She was indeed at home, seated at her writing-desk next to the fireplace, in the act of inscribing a note to Ellis Henlow. For the first time the sight of her *en négligé* did not move him in the least. She jumped at his entrance, and looked round, gaping in startled fear.

One glance at her face told Sothern all he needed to know. Cold fury seized him, more deadly than his earlier rage.

'You scheming, traitorous, lying bitch!'

He crossed the room, brushing past the chaise longue in which he had so often sat with this woman, amorously entwined. Without warning he seized her by the throat, dragging her half out of her chair.

'Who told you?' he demanded icily. Her terrified eyes goggled at him. 'Tell me, bitch. Before I squeeze the life out of you!'

'H-Henlow,' she croaked out.

Shock made him release her abruptly. She fell back into her chair, gasping for breath and putting her hands to her bruised throat.

'Ellis Henlow,' she gasped.

'My God!' Jake whispered, his fury giving place to lively apprehension. If Ellis Henlow was in town... His imagination boggled at the possibilities. And he had sworn to keep Clementina safe!

Without another word he turned on his heel, left the room, and ran down the stairs. He was at his grandmother's house in Brook Street in a matter of minutes, his horse in a lather of sweat.

Dorridge opened the door to him, adding to his anxiety with his first words of greeting.

'My lord! Thank heaven you are come! Her ladyship was on the point of sending for you.'

'Where is she?'

'Her ladyship is in the pink parlour, my lord. I will announce you.'

But Sothern was already at the pink parlour door. He entered to find his grandmother, in a state of great agitation, talking excitedly to his man of business. On a chair to one side sat the pathetic figure of Sir Jeremy Hythe, his gaunt face woebegone.

'Grandmama!'

As one, Lady Staplegrove and Mr Cullen turned. His grandmother hurried towards him.

'Jake, thank heaven!'

He began on an apology for breaking in on her in his riding dress, but she cut him short.

'Never mind that. What do I care for ceremony at such a time? Sothern, we are undone!'

'I know, Grandmama,' Jake said swiftly. 'And I know, too, who spread the tale.'

Lady Staplegrove looked astonished. 'What are you talking of?'

'Why, that the murder is out, of course.'

'Have you run mad, or have I?' demanded the dowager.

Jake blinked. 'You, I must suppose. What are *you* talking of?'

'Clementina, you ninny!' Lady Staplegrove threw up her hands. 'Oh, I've no patience! Tell him, Cullen.'

The lawyer coughed and adjusted his pince-nez. As Jake turned towards him his own eyes held a premonition of impending doom.

'My lord, Sir Jeremy came to me on a matter of the utmost urgency. Your wife, as I understand the erstwhile Miss Hythe to be, is in the gravest danger.'

Clementina sat at the table in a private parlour, lingering over the fruits and nuts, and eyeing Ellis Henlow's profile in a speculative way.

He had left the dinner table, and was engaged in writing his ransom note to Lord Sothern. He was not such a fool as to leave his back exposed to Clementina's possible revenge. From where he sat at the desk by the window he could still see her out of the corner of his eye and yet watch the approach to the courtyard of the George inn, should there by some remote chance have been any pursuit.

Henlow was not so confident, however, as to put up at the Fountain, the busy hostelry a few hundred yards up the road which, being a terminus for the London to Portsmouth stage-coach, took the main coaching trade. Here he was closer to the docks, however, which he persuaded himself was more suited to his purpose.

Clementina had felt little appetite, but she had forced herself to eat, albeit slowly. She needed strength if she was to find a means of escape. She prolonged the dinner in the hope of putting off the moment when Ellis might attempt to force his unwelcome attentions upon her. For she could not doubt that this was his intention. He meant to punish both herself and Sothern by this means, for he had told her that if the Earl failed to pay up he would take her abroad to live as his mistress, and so ruin her in any event.

All the way to Portsmouth she had spent the time weaving and discarding various impractical plans for escape. At the first change at the Bear inn at Esher, however, Ellis had made her remain in the coach, and stayed with her, his hand roughly grasping her neck.

'Make one move, one sound, and I'll choke you,' he'd promised coolly.

So Clementina had perforce stayed quiet, hardly daring to breathe, never mind cause a commotion. When they were held up by a herd of cattle wandering about the road while the drover refreshed himself at a nearby alehouse she'd had some idea of leaping from the coach and dodging among the cows. But the way was cleared before she had even begun to formulate a coherent plan.

There was no chance at the Talbot Inn at Ripley for the next change, and they swept through Guildford—a larger town where she had hoped it might prove easier to run away and hide—without a check. But at Godalming the passengers finally alighted to partake of a luncheon at the King's Arms. Clementina was too hungry to think much about escape, and she heard with a sinking heart that the next stage was a long one. The King's Arms was a busy posting-house, but Ellis never left her side for a moment, accompanying her even to the ladies' retiring-room where he waited for her outside.

She resumed the journey in a despondent mood which was not alleviated by the wild and desolate nature of the countryside through which they passed. There was scarcely a habitation to be seen for mile upon dreary mile, past pine woods and Witley Common, to the Devil's Punch Bowl with its gruesome gibbet at the top of Hindhead Hill. Clementina shuddered, glad of the presence on the road of the many other vehicles they met or passed. She was so relieved to arrive at the Anchor Inn at Liphook, with the very beautiful spreading chestnut in front of its Queen Anne façade offering so ordinary a welcome even in the now gathering dusk, that no thought of trying to get away entered her head.

By the time they finally got to Portsmouth she was so weary that even had she thought of a plan she doubted her ability to carry it through. But dinner had revived her, and she was ready for action. Besides, without the constant motion necessitated by a long journey she stood more chance of success. Even so, she cursed the hampering skirts of her morning dress, and longed for the freedom of Jeremy's borrowed breeches. Since their arrival here Ellis had continued in his role of gaoler, and had not for a moment left her alone. And now the door was locked, and he was still watching her as he wrote.

She wanted to scream, to spit at him and claw furrows with her nails into his handsome countenance. But he was so much stronger than she, and she knew that he would not balk at violence. Outside his father's restraining presence he would not curb his passions.

He finished his letter, folded it, and wrote the direction on the outside. Then he rose and crossed to the fireplace to tug on the bell-pull.

'You will have to unlock the door,' Clementina observed.

Ellis dipped a hand into his pocket and brought out the key, holding it up. 'Time enough when the servant arrives.'

'He will think it odd.'

'What business is it of his?'

Clementina shrugged. 'None, I suppose. I had not thought it any part of your design to draw attention upon us, however.'

He seemed to feel the force of this, for he smiled grimly, tossed the key in his hand, and then crossed to fit it into the lock. He looked back at her.

'No tricks,' he said warningly.

She shrugged again. 'What can I do?'

'Well, don't scream. I shall merely tell them we have quarrelled.' He paused, and his next words were softly menacing. 'And then beat the living daylights out of you.'

Clementina shivered. She could not doubt that he would carry out his threat. It was growing late, and she was growing desperate. She must do something. She heard footsteps coming up the stairs, approaching the door. Then the click as Henlow turned the key in the lock.

She rose from her chair. 'Ellis, I need the closet.'

'You will have to wait.''

'But I cannot.' She moved round the table and took up a stance before it, her hand feeling behind her on the cloth which still covered the table. 'Can't you escort me and wait outside the door?'

Ellis threw up his eyes. 'You are a confounded nuisance. Very well.'

There was a knock at the door. As Ellis turned to open it Clementina's fingers found the pepperpot. It was her only opportunity.

As Ellis stepped back to allow the servant to enter Clementina ran forwards, and bringing her hand from behind her back she dashed the contents of the pepper-pot full into Ellis Henlow's face.

He fell back with a roar of anguish, his hands flying to his burning eyes. The footman stood with mouth agape until two small hands heaved him to one side.

Clementina was out of the door and flying down the stairs, Ellis's bellows of agony ringing in her ears. Down the hall she sped, out of the inn door. Heedless of the ostlers and coachmen lounging about the yard, who watched her hurtling progress with varying expressions of astonishment, Clementina ran as for her life, all her tiredness forgotten as she determined to lose herself among the throng on the nearby quayside.

She hardly heard the rattle of hooves as she came out of the yard of the George on to the roadside. Picking up her skirts, she made to fly incontinently across the road, and was brought up short by an irate curse and the sudden realisation that a team of horses was about to run her down.

The driver pulled them up sharply, and Clementina jumped back on to the verge as the horses reared and their legs flailed alarmingly above her. In a moment they were under control, but the next second she was being shouted at.

'Hell and the devil, you idiotic wench! What in Hades are you about?'

She looked up at the man. In the same instant that she recognised the voice she saw his face.

'Jake! Oh, Jake!'

Lord Sothern, suddenly recognising his wife, gave out another oath, threw the reins to his groom, and leapt out of the phaeton.

'Clementina! Oh, God, Clementina!' he cried.

Then she was in his arms, crushed against his chest, laughing and crying together.

'Clementina,' he uttered into her hair, his tone anguished. 'Oh, my darling, I thought I had lost you!'

'I never thought you'd come,' she sobbed. 'I thought you'd be too late.'

He hugged her tighter, kissing her hair, her forehead. Then, pulling away a little to look into her face, he saw the tears on her cheeks, and cradled her face with one hand.

'Sweetheart, don't cry. You're safe now.'

'I know,' Clementina said, smiling through her tears. 'And I'm so happy!'

Jake kissed her. A long, lingering kiss that told her everything that was in his heart.

The sound of heavy feet, running, brought them apart. Clementina pulled herself out of his arms and turned.

'Ellis,' she cried, seeing the man approaching fast. 'I had forgotten him.'

Jake put her roughly behind him. 'Go into the inn. I'll deal with Henlow.'

He moved forward, purposefully removing his greatcoat and tossing it aside as Ellis Henlow came out into the road. The man's eyes were red and raw, his comely features contorted into ugliness with pain and fury. Seeing Sothern, he stopped short. Then something like a snarl left his throat, and he started towards the Earl.

'God damn you to hell!' he swore.

'You first, you lily-livered poltroon!' returned the Earl furiously.

It was not so much a fight as a slaughter. Ellis was a big man, but Jake was the taller and stronger of the two. Furthermore, like most fashionable males, he was accustomed to taking boxing lessons for sport, and was a frequent visitor to Mendoza's teaching establishment.

Ellis was met with a smashing right and left that sent him reeling back into the inn yard. Jake followed him, ready for more. Shaking his head to clear it, Ellis roared his fury and bored in again.

Jake took a blow to the jaw and his head snapped back. But he came up fast, ducking the flailing fists, and, punching for the stomach, got his man in a clinch and threw him a cross-buttock.

For a moment Ellis lay winded at his feet, while Jake stood over him, fists ready-clenched, scowling. Then, with a sudden lunge at the Earl's knees, Henlow brought him down. Both men rolled on the ground, but Ellis soon discovered his mistake.

Livid now, Jake exerted all his strength to roll the other under him. Then he grabbed the man's ears and, forcibly lifting his head, banged it back down on the rough cobbles of the inn yard. Leaping to his feet, he dragged the half-conscious man bodily up only so that he might crash his fist into the middle of his face and floor him again.

He heard the bone crunch under his hand, and knew that the famed looks were despoiled forever. Ellis Henlow lay senseless on the ground, bleeding copiously from his broken nose.

Breathing hard, Jake stepped back. In a gesture infinitely contemptuous, he dusted off his hands. A spatter of applause made him turn. All the coachmen and ostlers from the inn had come out into the yard to watch. In the middle of them was Clementina, her arms full with his greatcoat, her face flushed with excitement, clapping with the rest.

He grinned and went up to her. 'You're incorrigible. I told you to go inside.'

'Are you hurt?' she asked, ignoring his strictures.

Gingerly he felt his chin and moved his jaw. 'Somewhat.'

There was blood on his lip. Clementina reached up to wipe it away with her finger. Jake clasped her hand and kissed it. He glanced ruefully down at his person. He was covered in dirt, his clothes were awry and his neck-cloth all but ruined.

'My costume is more damaged than I, I fear. But it was undoubtedly worth it!'

'Come into the inn and we will soon amend it,' Clementina said unconcernedly. She glanced down at the wreck of the man who had caused her so much anguish. 'I thought you were going to kill him.'

'I very nearly did. I think it will be some time, however, before he is ready to beguile any other ladies.'

'He never beguiled me!' Clementina protested indignantly.

Jake took her hand and squeezed it. 'For which I thank God.'

She met his eyes, her lips quivering. 'No, that was left for you to do, my lord.'

His eyebrow lifted. 'Have I met with any success?'

'Oh, you are victor in all things today,' she told him, her eyes twinkling.

His hand tightened about hers. 'Then let us go in at once. I will be requiring further proofs as soon as may be convenient!'

Giggling, Clementina allowed him to pull her into the George, where she led him to the private parlour lately vacated by her erstwhile captor. Here Jake took her in his arms, despite spoiled clothes and an aching jaw, and for a few blissful moments they were the only two people in the world.

Then Jake rang for some refreshment and hot water, and, stripping off his coat, desired the waiter to have it cleaned and pressed. While he dusted off his boots and breeches and retied his neckcloth Clementina pelted him with questions, and learned how poor, confused Jeremy, not understanding any of it, but finally overcome with the idea that he had somehow betrayed Clementina, had sought out Mr Cullen. Fortunately the coachman had remembered the direction that Clementina had given him, and had driven him to Cullen's premises after Jeremy had urgently repeated his request to be taken to the lawyer.

It seemed that Ellis Henlow's abduction of Clementina was the act of a desperate man, Sothern told her.

'Cullen tells me that Major Henlow has already gone abroad to escape his creditors. Mrs Henlow is hiding out at Dunhythe, but has the intention to follow him as soon as may be. Ellis borrowed Jeremy, we think unbeknown to his mother, in order to perpetrate his evil design.'

'Poor Jeremy!' said Clementina distressfully. 'And his mother is going? How could she leave him to his own devices at Dunhythe?'

'She is a cruel woman,' the Earl stated.

Clementina laid down the clothes brush with which—in a very housewifely manner as he'd teasingly asserted—she had been assisting him to clean up, and turned back to him impulsively.

'Jake, I promised I would help him. Would you mind if we used my inheritance? It is yours now, I suppose, but——'

'My darling, I don't want it. And you have no need of it now. Not all of it, in any event. We may give the estate to your poor Jeremy, and as much money as he needs to run it until the rents begin to come in.'

'And an annuity for Margery,' Clementina decided. 'And she may stay on at Dunhythe and take care of Jeremy.'

'An excellent suggestion.'

'And what will happen to Ellis, do you suppose?' she added, almost as an afterthought.

'I imagine he will board the next packet for France.' Jake smiled grimly. 'If he knows what is good for him.'

'And so we will be rid of them all,' Clementina said happily. 'Not Margery and Jeremy, of course. I don't mean them.'

These matters being settled to their mutual satisfaction, the Earl refreshed himself with a pint of ale, which did much to restore him, and in spite of Clementina's protests he kissed her again.

'I'm not that badly hurt,' he insisted, although he did let her go. He smiled into her eyes and spoke teasingly. 'I'll show you later just how little.'

Clementina blushed. 'Are we going home, then? To Albemarle Street?'

'No. We're going home to Berkshire. Now our secret is known we may as well give it out that we've gone on our honeymoon.'

'Very well,' she agreed equably. 'I don't care where we go. I just want to be with you. I love you, Jake.'

He made no move to touch her again, but his eyes held a warmth she had never seen there before.

'And I think I fell in love with you that very first night,' he said softly. 'When you faced us all so bravely.'

Clementina gave a rueful little laugh. 'I was petrified.'

'I know. And you'd have died before you let us see it, wouldn't you, my indomitable little love?'

She bit her lip. 'I'm still afraid.'

Jake's brows drew together in quick consternation. 'My darling, of what?'

Clementina came to him, and put her hands against his chest. He covered them reassuringly with his own and held them so.

'Jake, promise me one thing. If—when—you tire of me, tell me. Don't let me go on thinking; don't let me make a fool of myself. I won't fuss. I won't make scenes. Only as long as I know.'

The Earl's dark eyes shadowed with concern. 'Clementina, you don't see it, do you? My sweet, before you came into my life I had never truly loved any woman. I know that now.' His fingers caressed her cheek and his voice was tender. 'To love you, my Clementina, is to cherish you. Now and always.'

'Oh, Jake,' she sighed contentedly.

'So, you see, I'll never tire of you.' He grinned suddenly. 'Won't make scenes? If I ever dared to so much as look at another woman I shudder to think of the consequences!'

Clementina's lips quivered. He knew her all too well already. 'Then there is only one thing for it, my lord. Don't dare!'

And they were both laughing.

Experience the thrill of 2 Masquerade Historical Romances Absolutely Free!

Experience the passions of bygone days
in 2 gripping Masquerade Romances - absolutely free!
Enjoy these tales of tempestuous love from
the illustrious past.
Then, if you wish, look forward to a regular supply of
Masquerade, delivered to your door!
Turn the page for details of 2 extra FREE gifts,
and how to apply.

An irresistible offer for you

Here at Reader Service we would love you to become a regular reader of Masquerade. And to welcome you, we'd like you to have two books, a cuddly teddy and a MYSTERY GIFT - ABSOLUTELY FREE and without obligation.

Then, every two months you could look forward to receiving 4 more brand-new Masquerade Romances for just £1.99 each, delivered to your door, postage and packing is free. Plus our free newsletter featuring competitions, author news, special offers offering some great prizes, and lots more!

This invitation comes with no strings attached. You can cancel or suspend your subscription at any time, and still keep your free books and gifts.

Its so easy. Send no money now. Simply fill in the coupon below at once and post it to - Reader Service, FREEPOST, PO Box 236, Croydon, Surrey CR9 9EL.

✂ - - - NO STAMP REQUIRED - - - ➤

Yes! Please rush me my 2 Free Masquerade Romances and 2 Free Gifts! Please also reserve me a Reader Service Subscription. If I decide to subscribe, I can look forward to receiving 4 brand new Masquerade Romances every two months for just £7.96, delivered direct to my door. Post and packing is free, and there's a free Newsletter. If I choose not to subscribe I shall write to you within 10 days - I can keep the books and gifts whatever I decide. I can cancel or suspend my subscription at any time. I am over 18.

Mrs/Miss/Ms/Mr _____ EP05M

Address _____

_____

_____ Postcode _____

Signature _____

mps
MAILING
PREFERENCE
SERVICE